D1266050

Astronomer Priest and Ancient Mariner

LANCELOT HOGBEN

Astronomer Priest and Ancient Mariner

ST. MARTIN'S PRESS : NEW YORK

HARDEMAN COUNTY LIBRARY
QUANAH, TEXAS

Copyright © 1973 by Lancelot Hogben
All rights reserved. For information, write:
St. Martin's Press, Inc., 175 Fifth Ave., New York, N.Y. 10010
Printed in Great Britain
Library of Congress Catalog Card Number: 73-83766
First published in the United States of America in 1973

Contents

Acknowledgements   vi

Illustrations   vii

Foreword   xi

Chapter 1   1
The Coming of the Calendar

Chapter 2   18
Pyramids and Temples

Chapter 3   43
The Legacy of the Temple

Chapter 4   60
The Greek Contribution

Chapter 5   76
The Ancient Mariner

Chapter 6   93
Maritime Geography and Maritime Astronomy

Acknowledgements

The author is indebted to the following for permission to reproduce pictures on the pages indicated: Aerofilms, 32; George Allen & Unwin Ltd, 34, 50, 51, 54, 56, 57, 77, 104; British Tourist Authority, 33; The Trustees of the British Museum, 19, 20, 47, 61, 62, 65, 67; CBS Television Network, 35; Les Chefs-d'Oeuvre de la Peinture Egyptienne, Andre Lhote (Librairie Hachette, Paris), 54; Cia Mexicana Aerofoto, 20; Encyclopaedia Britannica, 27; Her Majesty's Stationery Office, 10, 11; Macdonald & Co. Ltd, 24, 26, 44, 45, 52; Mansell Collection, 109; N. G. Matthew Esq, 2, 3, 4, 5; Mexican National Tourist Council, 21; Paul Popper (Popperfoto), 22, 104; Peabody Museum of Archaeology and Enthnology, Harvard University, 21; Prehistoric Society, 36; The Trustees of the Science Museum, London, 49, 60, 71, 105, (Crown Copyright, 49, 71); Staatliche Museen Preussischer Kulturbesitz, Berlin, 73.

Illustrations

Chapter 1
  1. Night sky at latitude of London at mid-March
  2. Night sky at latitude of London at mid-June
  3. Night sky at latitude of London at mid-September
  4. Night sky at latitude of London at mid-December
  5. (a) Apparent diurnal motion of the stars
     (b) The changing heavens
  6. (a) Night Dial
     (b) Night Dial in use
  7. The sun's (apparent) annual retreat through the zodiacal constellations
  8. The monthly cycle of the moon's phases
  9. (a) The Egyptian year
     (b) Heliacal rising and setting of a star

Chapter 2
  10. (a) Ziggurat at Ur as it looked after excavations of Woolley
      (b) Reconstruction of ziggurat
  11. (a) Tectihuacán, Mexico, from the air
      (b) Mayan stele at Quirigua, Guatemala
  12. (a) Mayan Temple of Warriors
      (b) The Caracol, an observatory at Chicken Itza, Yucatan
  13. Pyramid of Khehren
  14. Karnak Mathematics in the Making
  15. The three pyramids of Gizeh
  16. Centre section of the Great Pyramid of Khufu, Gizeh, *c*. 3000 B.C.
  17. (a) Aerial view of Stonehenge
      (b) Ground view of Stonehenge
  18. Heel Stone, Stonehenge
  19. Sunrise on midsummer day, Stonehenge
  20. Plan of the stones and excavated areas, Stonehenge

21. Aubrey holes, an eclipse clock, as interpreted by Professor Hawkins

Chapter 3
22. Egyptian hieroglyphic writing, showing numerals.
23. (a) Cuneiform Tablet
    (b) Old Babylonian cuneiform script
24. Rhind papyrus
25. Reconstruction of ancient Egyptian *merkhet*
26. *Merkhet* and *bay*—one use of the plumbline in ancient Egypt
27. Bisecting a line
28. Speculative reconstruction of the Set Square of the Temple Architects
29. (a) Diagram showing means of measuring noon shadow
    (b) Temple Architects recording of equinoctial positions
30. Fifteenth century B.C. Egyptian surveying, from a wall painting
31. Diagram showing measurement of the noon shadow cast by the Great Pyramid at Gizeh
32. The Abacus
    (a) Roman
    (b) Chinese
    (c) Japanese

Chapter 4
33. Egyptian sea-going ship (*c.* 2600 B.C.)
34. Phoenician warship
35. Phoenician bracelet
36. Phoenician script
37. (a) Greek sea-going vessel, vase painting
    (b) Greek Galley

38. Early Greek drama
39. Cast of water clock from Karnak
40. Masters and pupils at an Athenian school

Chapter 5
41. The visible limits of the horizon
42. Map of the Mediterranean
43. Southern Cross
44. Map of Europe
45. Map of Africa

Chapter 6
46. Eclipses
47. Moon eclipse, seen in East Germany
48. Solar eclipse
49. Inclination of the moon's track to the Ecliptic
50. Romantic nineteenth century engraving of how Greeks imagined the Pillars of Hercules

Foreword

I am sure that most younger people are much more familiar with the contemporary term Iraq than with the ancient names of Chaldea, Babylonia, Mesopotamia and Assyria. I therefore refer to Iraq when writing of the temple sites in these regions.

Some scientists are most reluctant to recognise the great antiquity of star lore and the important part it plays in the struggle for existence of people who, even at the start of this century, lived in a way scarcely more sophisticated than that of men and women on the threshold of the New Stone Age. Dr Nilsson, a Swedish scientist, has collected available material from many sources in a treatise on *Primitive Time Reckoning*, from which these quotes are taken (words in parenthesis inserted):

"Observation of the morning rising and evening setting (*of fixed stars*) is extraordinarily widespread, but other positions of the stars . . . are also sometimes observed. The Krivai Papuans (*New Guinea*) also compute the time of invisibility of a star. When a star has sunk below the western horizon, they wait for some nights during which the star is 'inside'; then it has 'made a leap' and shows itself in the east before sunrise . . . The Hottentots connect the Pleiades with winter. These stars (*at their latitude*) become visible in the middle of June, that is, in the first half of the cold season . . . The appearance of the Pleiades also gives the Bushman of the Anob district the signal for departure to the tsama field . . . The Melanesians of Banks Island and the Northern Hebrides are also acquainted with the Pleiades as a sign of the approach of the yam harvest. The inhabitants of New Britain (*Bismarck Archipelago*) are guided in ascertaining the time of planting by the position of certain stars."

Elsewhere, Dr Nilsson says of the star lore of the

Australian aborigines: "The winter stars are Arcturus, who is held in great respect since he has taught the natives to find the pupae of the wood-ants which are an important article of food in August and September (*Australian winter months*), and Vega, who has taught them to find the eggs of the mallee-hen . . . When Canopus at dawn is only a very little way above the eastern horizon, it is time to collect these eggs and pupae."

Writing of the natives of the Admiralty Islands, he states: "When the Bird (Canis major) is in such a position that one wing points north but the other is invisible, the time has come in which the turtles lay eggs, and many natives then go to the Los-Reys group in order to collect them." Of the natives in the Bougainville Straits (off Queensland) Nilsson mentions that the rising of the Pleiades "is sign that the Kai-nut is ripe".

The first volume in this series, *Beginnings and Blunders,* traced the story of the skills our ancestors acquired, and the skulls they left in their wake, before science began. This book starts with the need for a calendar to regulate the seasonal order of seed-sowing and flock-tending. For the construction of such a calendar men of the New Stone Age doubtless drew on the knowledge gained throughout many millennia from the scanning of the night skies by men who were still nomads and from the observation of the sun's seasonal changes when village life began. The art of keeping a written record of the lapse of time took shape about 5000 years ago and was the achievement of the priestly guardians of the calendar in the temple sites of Egypt and Iraq. An incidental, but not itself useful, by-product of this phase of infant science was the art of forecasting correctly the occurrence of eclipses.

By 1000 B.C. ships from the trading centres of the Mediterranean had travelled beyond the Pillars of Hercules (Straits of Gibraltar) and literate Master Mariners, who relied on star lore to navigate, could record, by a new and more economical way of writing—alphabetic—how the aspect of the heavens changes with latitude. A compelling consequence of such observations materialised by about 500 B.C. in the recognition that the earth is a spherical body. *Astronomer Priest and Ancient Mariner* brings the reader to this stage in the history of science.

Lancelot Hogben

1 The Coming of the Calendar

As most of us nowadays use the word *science,* and as we shall use it in this book, one may say that it began when men were first able to record in writing their observations on their surroundings and to convey in writing a picture of the world as they saw it and with some pay-off in the world's work.

This happened at least 5000 years ago in the city temples beside the Nile in Egypt and in Iraq by the rivers Tigris and Euphrates. During at least 4000 years where life was cheap and slave labour abundant there was no science of medicine and very little scientific mechanics. What science existed was what we now call astronomy and closely allied studies. The pay-off in the world's work was how to find our way about in time and space, in short, to devise a reliable calendar and to draw a map of the planet we inhabit.

Most of us realise, at least vaguely, that our calendar depends on observation of a regular recurrence of the changing appearance of the night sky and the sun's highest elevation above the horizon. To many of us, however, it may seem paradoxical that man had to learn how to make a map of the heavens before he was able to make a map of the earth.

Observations on the changes of the night sky and of the sun by day did not begin as the result of the introduction of writing. On the contrary, the imperative need for recording them was a powerful impetus to devising the most primitive scripts. Villagers of the New Stone Age, whose dwellings and allotments coalesced to form the cities where the priestly caste had leisure to record the vagaries of sun, moon and stars, had received from their ancestors a rich legacy of information transmitted from one generation to another by word of mouth.

Even in our own century, there have survived outside

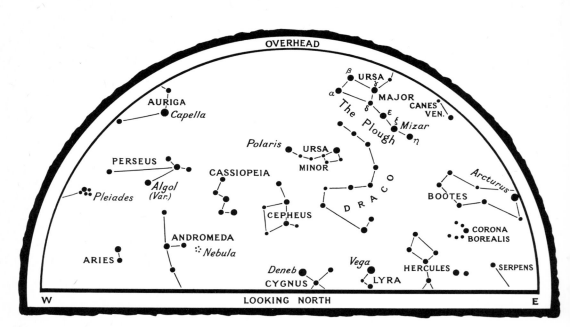

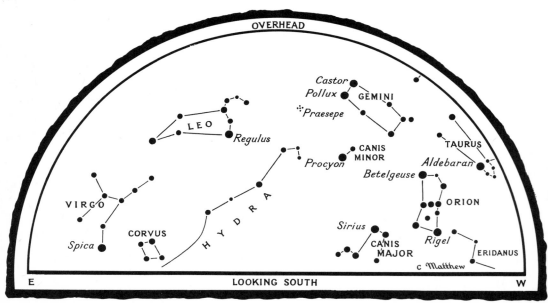

1. Night sky at latitude of
   London at mid-March

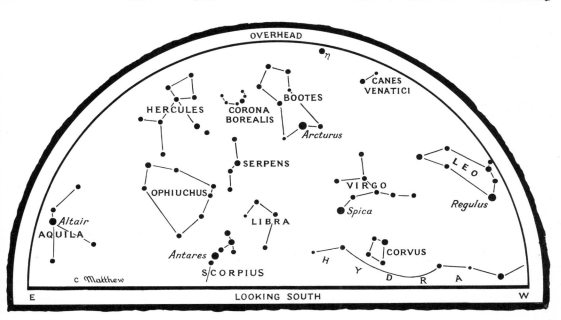

2. Night sky at latitude of
London at mid-June

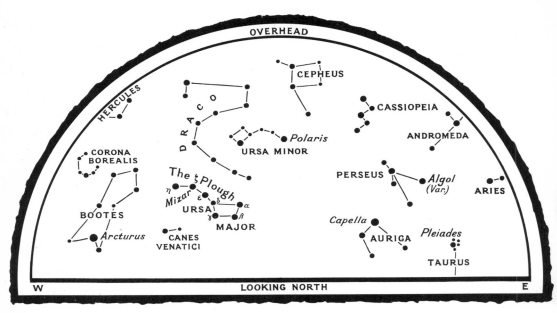

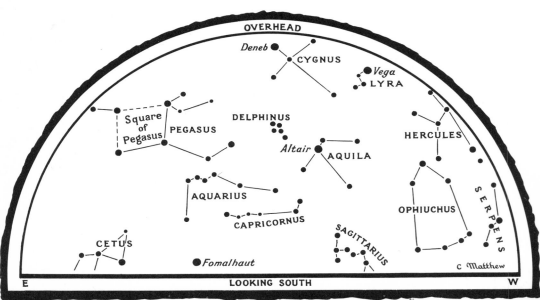

3. Night sky at latitude of
   London at mid-
   September

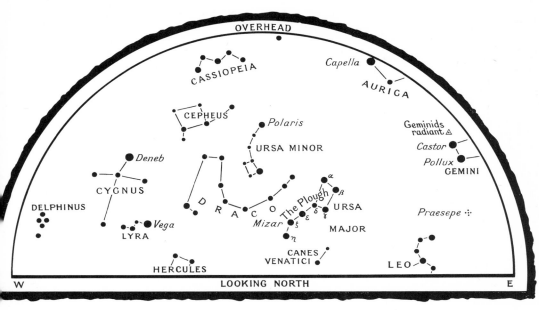

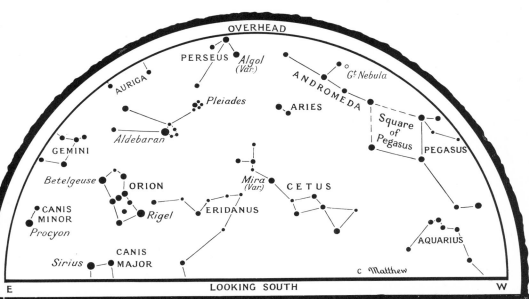

4. Night sky at latitude of London at mid-December

the pale of civilisation people who wander in search of food as did nomadic tribes of the Old Stone Age before village life began, and such folk know vastly more about the changing aspect of the night sky throughout the seasons than do the vast majority of people who grow up to-day in cities. It is not hard to understand why they have such knowledge, and hence to reconstruct the traditional store of knowledge which the priestly astronomers of the earliest cities inherited from millennia of observation by their ancestors.

Without roads and without maps, nomads of the Old Stone Age from at least 25,000 years ago had to learn where and when to locate camping sites where game, eggs, berries and edible grasses were available as their only source of food. Without clocks, without calendars and without maps they had to learn both how to date the trek to new hunting grounds in the season at which food was abundant and to locate their sites.

To do either, they had to rely on the aspect of the sky. Sitting beside the camp fire in the hours of darkness, our Old Stone Age ancestors would learn to memorise landmarks on the horizon by the rising and setting position of bright stars such as Sirius or bright star clusters such as Orion or the Pleiades. They would learn to keep track of the seasons by the day on which one such star or constellation was first visible rising or setting just before sunrise or just after sunset.

Such events were their signals of when to strike camp and whither to trek. At a time when each tribe enjoyed the patronage of its own sacred animal fancifully identified with a particular star cluster—such as *Aries* (the Ram), *Taurus* (the Bull), *Cancer* (the Crab), *Leo* (the Lion), *Scorpio* (the Scorpion) in the zodiacal belt—the first appearance of a constellation was also the time signal for the sacrificial feast of a victim otherwise immune from attack throughout the year. Such is a practice among letterless people still living. Then, as now, tribal ritual also dictated elaborate ceremonies associated with sexual maturity. The elders of the tribe had to enumerate how many moons elapsed between birth and the initiation.

Many readers of this book will have grown up in surroundings where tall buildings obscure the horizon in every direction. They will have had no opportunities to watch what positions the stars occupy at different times on the same night or at the same time on different nights. It is therefore fitting to start the story of how science began by scanning the night sky through the eyes of Stone Age men and women for whom trees and hillocks on the horizon of the camping site labelled the rising or setting positions of the heavenly bodies.

The first city dwellers, who were able to record in writing the fruit of many millennia of nightly vigils, themselves lived in the northern hemisphere. So we need concern ourselves only with the night sky of northern latitudes. First, let us be clear about the distinction between two sorts of heavenly bodies respectively called fixed stars and planets. In terms of what the night watchman can see for himself or herself, one calls the stars fixed because the rising and setting positions of each one correspond at any camp site to the same two land marks.

The planets, of which only Venus, Jupiter and Mars are conspicuous to the naked eye, are not fixed in this sense. However, we shall need to bear in mind that the term *fixed* is relative to the lifetime of a few generations. To the naked eye, the rising and setting positions of stars at one and the same latitude do not detectably shift in a century. In a millennium, they do so conspicuously.

Though they do not vary perceptibly within the limits of a single trek of tribes with no means of transport other than their own limbs, they vary greatly in widely separated latitudes, a fact on which the mariner has to rely for his bearings when he ventures into the unknown.

We now know that the shifting position of the stars at rising or setting and their elevation when highest in the heavens happens in cycles which occupy between 25,000 and 26,000 years, and the first Cave Painters—people of our own species—appear on the scene about 25,000 years ago. So we may speak of the aspect of our own night sky as essentially like that of the first artists.

At one and the same latitude, the fixed stars are separable into two groups. Those of one class, such as Sirius or the stars in Orion at the latitudes of London and New York in our life-time, are seen at some seasons rising or setting or both during the hours of darkness, but at another season invisible throughout the night. At the same latitudes today, the other class, called *circumpolar* stars, such as those (Figs. 1–4) of the cluster *Ursa Major* (the Great Bear) also called The Plough or The Dipper are visible at all hours of a clear night and at all seasons.

At the present time, as in the time of the first Cave Painters, one star in the northern half of the sky is of special interest. It is at the tail end (Figs. 1–4) of the constellation *Ursa Minor* (the Little Bear). To the naked eye it seems to remain at the same spot at all times when visible.

With optical instruments, we should find that it is not truly fixed in this sense. It is indeed a circumpolar star which rotates through a complete circle in 24 hours like other circumpolar stars, but very near to its centre, an imaginary point known as the *Celestial Pole*. Only because its circular track is relatively so small does it seem to the naked eye to remain fixed at all hours and throughout the year.

Round this star, called by astronomers *Polaris* and by others the Mariner's Pole Star, or more precisely round the Celestial Pole as centre, the visible circumpolar stars seem to revolve, and other stars when visible above the horizon appear to sweep out circular arcs tilted towards the southern margin of the sky (Figs 5a and 5b). Facing

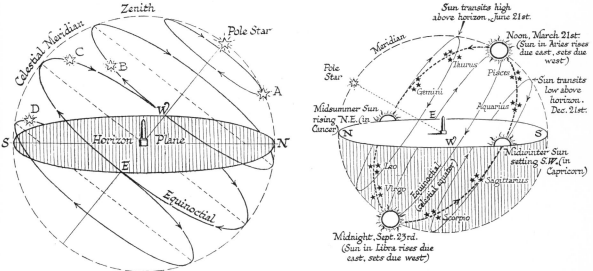

5. (a) Apparent diurnal motion of the stars
   (b) The changing heavens

north, i.e. towards the circumpolar constellations, the Old Stone Age night watcher would see other stars rising towards his right hand and setting towards his left. Facing south, i.e. towards the opposite boundary of the horizon, he would see stars rising towards his left hand and setting towards his right. He would thus learn to distinguish an *easterly* and a *westerly* boundary to the horizon at whatever site the tribe bivouacked.

Unwittingly, Stone Age Man has thus learned to orientate himself in the plane of the horizon by reference to a North-South axis—we now call it the *terrestrial meridian*—and an East-West axis at right angles to it. He has also gained a new awareness of the passage of time. The position of the clock hands of a circumpolar constellation, such as the Great Bear (*Dipper*) in our epoch, tells him how far or near is the hour of dawn (Figs 6a and 6b).

6. (a) Night Dial (for use see 6(b))

The first dwellers in villages, the men of the New Stone Age, had opportunities of leisure to make other discoveries, more especially about the apparent motion of the sun and the moon. They would notice that the

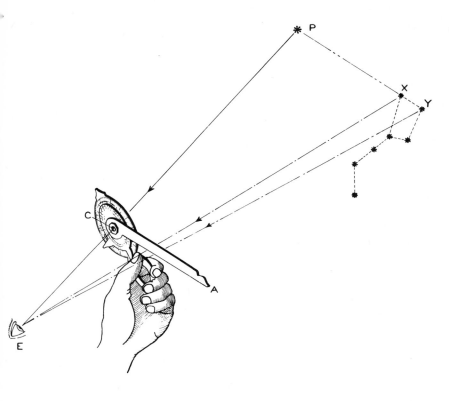

(b) The stars marked
     X and Y are the
     clock stars of the
     Great Bear. P is
     the Pole Star

length of the sun's shadow after dawn first decreases,
then increases, being shortest when pointing due north
in the northern hemisphere where village life began.
They would thus divide the daylight interval into two
parts, one from sunrise to noon, the other from noon to
sundown.

   They would also notice that the sun's position relative
to the fixed stars changes in two ways. One is that a star
which rises on the eastern boundary just before sunrise
on a particular day will be seen well above the horizon a
few days later. In short, the sun seems to be slipping
below the eastern horizon day by day. As it does so,
(Fig. 7), its rising and setting positions correspond to
those of different constellations, those we call the *zodiac*.

They would thus begin to recognise another thing about the sun's seemingly annual track (Fig. 8). When its rising and setting positions are furthest north, the sun's noon shadow is shorter than at any other time. The hours of daylight are then longest and the earth is warmer. When the sun's rising and setting positions are furthest south, its noon shadow is longest, the hours of daylight shortest and the weather cooler. Midway between the longest day, called midsummer or the *summer solstice* and the shortest day, called midwinter or the *winter solstice,* are the spring and autumn *equinoxes* when the sun's rising and setting positions are almost exactly due east and due west. On these two days, the hours of light and darkness are almost exactly equal. In our calendar, the solstices are June 21 and December 21, the equinoxes March 21 and September 23.

7. The sun's (apparent) annual retreat through the zodiacal constellations (The South Pole of the earth is nearest to you in the figure.)

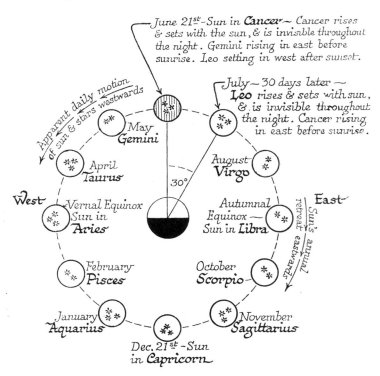

June 21st - Sun in **Cancer** ~ Cancer rises & sets with the sun, & is invisible throughout the night. Gemini rising in east before sunrise. Leo setting in west after sunset.

July — 30 days later — Leo rises & sets with sun, & is invisible throughout the night. Cancer rising in east before sunrise.

Apparent daily motion of sun & stars westwards

May Gemini

April Taurus

30°

West

Vernal Equinox Sun in Aries

February Pisces

January Aquarius

Dec. 21st - Sun in Capricorn

November Sagittarius

October Scorpio

Autumnal Equinox — Sun in Libra

August Virgo

East

Sun's annual retreat eastwards

The word *almost* used twice in the last paragraph is a warning signal. Because we learn in childhood that the sun rises in the east and sets in the west, many town-bred people take the catchphrase to mean that it rises due east and sets due west daily throughout the year. The statement as it stands is approximately true only of two days in the year, i.e. the equinoxes. Even if the sun on the equinox of a particular year rises exactly due east, it could not set exactly due west on the same day. Like-wise, should it set exactly due west, it could not have risen exactly due east on the same day. The reason is that the sun's position relative to the earth is changing, albeit slightly, between sunrise and sunset.

Just as the sun's rising and setting positions change in its annual cycle, the moon's rising and setting positions also change in the cycle (Fig. 8) between one full moon

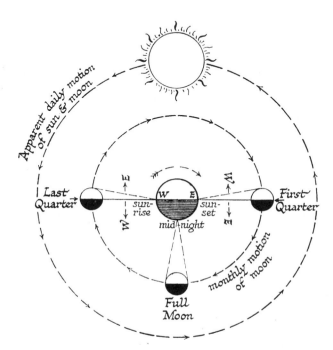

8. The monthly cycle of the moon's phases

and another. It seems to be slipping daily a little further below the eastern horizon, as does the sun, but more rapidly than the sun does. We can defer the details of the track it follows till we learn a little about the pre-occupation of the priests with lunar and solar eclipses in the dawn of city life.

Before village life began, we may be certain that the elders of the tribe had learned to reckon time in terms of the interval between one full (or one new) moon and the next, i.e. a month.* At what stage men recognised the month as approximately 30 days and the complete cycle of the season as approximately 12 such months, we do not certainly know. What is certain is that an annual calendar was an imperative need of a seasonal economy of agriculture, and that any measure of the year more sophisticated than the 360 day cycle of the priestly astronomers of Iraq made prohibitive demands on the memory of those responsible for keeping track of the seasons.

Long before the building (3000–2500 B.C.) of the Pyramids the Egyptian year (Figs. 9a and 9b) of 12 thirty-day months and 5 extra days, i.e. 365 days in all, had been fixed as the interval between successive occasions when Sirius, brightest of all the stars, was visible just above the horizon immediately before sunrise. That such precision was possible depends partly on two facts. The dog star Sirius, being the brightest star in the firmament, is visible in twilight before any other fixed star, and twilight is much shorter, nearer the tropical Belt than in the prosperous centres of modern civilisation. The Egyptian

*By a study of bones, pieces of rock and wood with regularly indented notches in groups separated by intervals, Alexander Marshack (1970) has recently made a strong case for the conclusion that people from the earliest appearance of man as a picture maker some 30,000 years ago kept tallies of the moon's phases as a means of counting the months.

estimate of the year, probably made as early as 4241 B.C.,
is equivalent to our own estimate except in so far as we
insert a leap year to accommodate the fact that the
interval between noon on successive solstices is almost

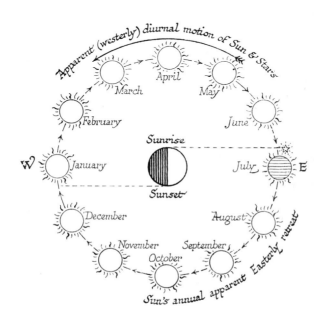

9. (a) The Egyptian year

exactly 365¼ days.

The possibility of such precision at so early a date does
not depend merely on the brightness of Sirius and short
duration of twilight. It presupposes the means of making
a record. Counting 365 successive days is not like counting 365 sheep in the same field at the same time. Without
some material aid to the memory, it would overtax the
mental powers of the wisest elder of the village com-
munity. We can indeed make a good guess about how he
or she tackled the task.

We are all familiar with the Roman numerals still
sometimes used for chapter headings and on sundials. In
their earliest form, as is true of the Egyptian and Baby-

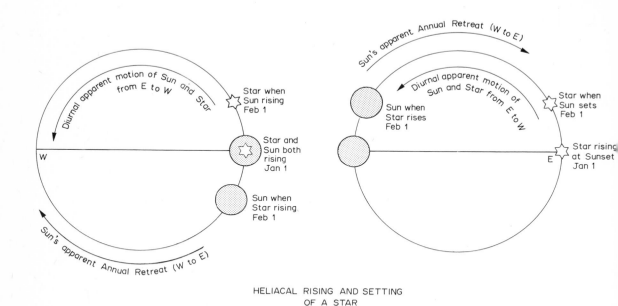

HELIACAL RISING AND SETTING
OF A STAR

(b) Heliacal rising and
     setting of a star

Ionian numerals of the temple sites, they followed a consistently repetitive plan, e.g. Roman VIIII for later IX. This fact strongly suggests that the pioneers of the earliest annual calendar counted off the days by chipping notches on a pillar or slab of stone or wood, as schoolboy onlookers now make strokes on paper to score runs at a cricket match.

As village communities became larger and coalesced on the banks of great rivers—Nile, Tigris, Euphrates, Indus and the Yellow River (Hwang Ho) of China, there was increasing specialisation of tasks other than tilling the soil and herdmanship. Thus craftsmen with different skills undertook the building and surveying. A caste concerned with the custody of the calendar and the performance of the ritual of sacrifice and prayer associated with different celestial events gained increasing prestige and power to exact tribute from those who cultivated their allotments.

As they sacrificed and offered up prayers to their sky-born deities, they preyed more and more on the credulity of the farmers and artisans. Meanwhile, they had leisure to elaborate the art of recording and were thus the first class of literate persons. They supervised the construction of gigantic buildings in honour of supposedly sky-born rulers who were, in effect, the highest order of priesthood. As we shall see, their design had a special relation to the events of the calendar. It gave impetus both to geometrical discoveries and continuing astronomical study.

In the days of the pyramid architects, it was customary to group the months in 3 sets of 4, named as seasons of flooding, sowing and harvesting. The Egyptian name for the first of the three seasons suggests what tradition has preserved. In the time of the earliest custodians of the calendar, the first sight of the dog star just before dawn corresponded with the annual rising of the Nile. This flooded the banks where the tillers would later sow crops, and fertilised the soil anew by the silt which it brought from its source.

Needless to say, the length of the lunar cycle was not exactly 30 days as the priests of Egypt and Iraq estimated it to be. We now know that a trifle (actually 29.53) more than $29\frac{1}{2}$ days of 24-hour intervals by our reckoning, separates one new or full moon from the next. The true length of the month is thus a little nearer 30 than 29 days.

Several thousand years elapsed between the first written record of a calendar by the priestly astronomers of Egypt and Iraq and a new impetus to scientific curiosity from the emergence of a craft of literate master mariners. Chapter 2 examines the temples that also served as observatories during this interval.

B

2 Pyramids and Temples

In the clumsy scripts of documents and tablets which have come down to us intact from the ruins of temple libraries of Egypt and Iraq, we get some insight into the level of mathematical knowledge current among the temple architects, surveyors and astronomer priests in the first few thousand years of civilisation. If we ask ourselves how they built such vast tombs and even vaster temples, we can also gain much insight by studying their material achievements in massive masonry. Let us therefore think back to a time when architecture, calendar-making and the technique of keeping a permanent record of events were still facets of the same preoccupation.

A feature common to samples of such massive masonry characteristic of the two earliest civilisations of the Old World and the two best-known indigenous ones of the New, i.e. the Maya of Central America and the Toltec of Mexico, is the step-wise construction of terraces on a more or less quadrilateral lay-out, the whole being thus of diminishing horizontal dimensions in the upward direction. Such, for example, were the ziggurat (Figs 10a and 10b) temples of ancient Iraq. Such also were the earliest Egyptian Pyramids and the Mexican *step pyramids* which have been intensively studied only during the last fifty years (Figs 11a and 11b).

To say the least, it is highly probable that convenience for observation of astronomical phenomena relevant to calendar keeping dictated the terraced structure. That the temples of the Maya were essentially observatories is beyond dispute. As one expert remarks: "every piece of Mayan construction was part of a great calendar of stone". Huge stone pillars in the forecourts recorded in carved symbols a succession of dates since the time of construction. Even the number of steps in a stairway leading to the temple door might stand for days inter-

10. (a) Ziggurat at Ur as it looked after excavations of Woolley

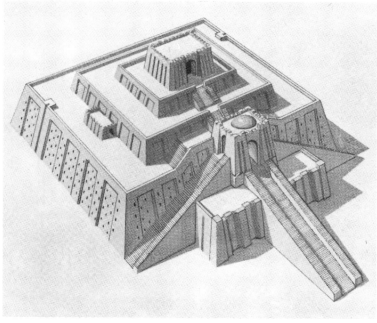

(b) Reconstruction of ziggurat

11. (a) Tectihuacán, Mexico, from the air. Foreground, Pyramid of the Moon, further away Pyramid of the Sun

(b) Mayan stele at Quirigua, Guatemala

calated for calendar adjustment (Figs. 12a and 12b).

From this point of view, the *Pyramid of the Serpent* excavated in 1925 on the North West Boundary of Mexico City is of special interest. As Ceram says, it is an an onion in stone. It consists of 8 shells, the smallest in the centre; and it appears that each shell records the Mexican *Calendar Round* of 52 years. The whole structure must have therefore taken over 400 years to complete. Some thirty miles away is another step pyramid 128 feet high. This is of height comparable to that of a ten-storey building. The area of the base of the largest of all the Mexican step pyramids is greater than that of the so-called Great Pyramid of Cheops at Gizeh (Fig. 13) a few miles outside Cairo.

There are also very good reasons for regarding the temples of the first city sites as observatories. In his treatise on the *Dawn of Astronomy* Sir Norman Lockyer,

12. (a) Mayan Temple of Warriors

(b) The Caracol, an observatory at Chicken Itza, Yucatan

13. Pyramid of Khehren

a former Astronomer Royal, puts the case thus: "there were sacrifices at daybreak . . . stars were watched before sunrise and heralded the dawn . . . these observations were among the chief duties of the sacrificial priests, and it is obvious that a knowledge of star-names must have been imperative to those morning watchers who eventually compiled lists . . . These are the exact equivalents of the moon-stations which the Indians and Arabians and other peoples invented for the purpose". Indeed, representations in ancient temples disclose the constellations of marker stars whose rising and setting positions tally with those of the sun in its annual track through the *Ecliptic* belt within the zodiacal constellations (p. 7).

As mentioned earlier, the fixed stars very slowly change their rising and setting positions on the horizon. So it is not certain what orientation corresponds to a particular star unless we know the date, or to a particular date unless we know the star. However, the inclination of the sun's apparent annual retreat, or as we now say, that of the earth's orbit, to the celestial equator has changed only very slightly in the whole of recorded history. As Sir Norman Lockyer puts it, "once a solar temple, a solar temple for thousands of years; once a star temple, only a star temple for something like 300 years". Indeed, there is reason to believe that some Egyptian star-set temples changed their allegiance after the lapse of centuries to greet the coming of new heavenly visitants.

When we speak of a solar temple of ancient Egypt, we must figure to ourselves an open door leading to a long corridor with the holiest place at the end of it (Fig. 14). We then envisage the placing of the portal and corridor so that only once a year a thin beam of light exactly at dawn, noon, or sundown could pass without interruption through the whole length of the corridor to the sanctuary in "most resplendent fashion", as Lockyer says, "striking the sanctuary wall". Egyptian solar temples might have the portal and corridor pointing direct east or west to sunrise or to sunset on the Equinoxes (March 21 and September 23). If so, their orientation raised a geometrical problem which we shall touch on later.

They might also face the rising or setting sun of the Summer Solstice (June 21 in our calendar). Such was the Egyptian New Year's Day. Alternatively, they might face dawn or sundown on the winter solstice (December 21).

14. Karnak Mathematics
     in the Making

Lockyer mentions six solstice temples, including an avenue of Sphinxes. Three of them were at Karnak. Of these three, two faced sunset on midsummer day, one greeted midwinter sunrise. The great temple of the sun in Peking, China, greets the rising sun of the winter solstice. On a plain near Thebes in South Egypt with faces turned towards sunrise on that day were two colossal images of the Pharaoh Amen-hotep III. Each was 60 feet high and cut from a single rock.

The step pyramids of Mexico, like the ziggurats, were observatory temples. The step pyramids of Egypt and their smooth-faced successors at Gizeh were essentially burial mounds for divine Kings; but each was in close propinquity to a temple devoted to his worship in the east-west axis of the latter. Seemingly the worshippers entered the temple from the East, facing west towards the Sarcophagus. Typically, the north face of the pyramid had a passage leading down to a burial chamber.

The Great Pyramid of Cheops (Khufu) at Gizeh is of about the height of a 40-storey building, well above that of St. Paul's Cathedral in London. One observer cites the mean error of the base angles in comparison with those of a perfect square to be about one three hundredth of a degree and the mean error of the lengths to be little more than half an inch. As regards placing of the sides with reference to the so-called compass points, the angular error, according to the same source, is little more than a thousandth of a degree.

Of the three larger pyramids of Gizeh still standing (Fig. 15), two had attendant groups of three smaller ones, possibly for royal ladies. The mean inclination of the faces of the former was about 50° to the base. For that of Cheops it was 51.85°. A peculiar feature of two large pyramids, Sneferu at Medum and Cheops at Gizeh, is

15. The three pyramids of
    Gizeh

that the ratio of the base to the height is 11:7. That of
twice the base to the height is thus 22:7, i.e. the numerical approximation we now first learn to use at school for
π. So the ratio of the perimeter of the base to the height
is a very close approximation to the ratio of the circum-
ference to the radius of a circle. This has no known
astronomical significance and has prompted fruitless
speculation, some of it silly.

The internal structure (Fig. 16) of the Great Pyramid of
Cheops is more complex than that of the others. The
centrally placed entrance faced north, as was commonly
so; and the passage therefrom descended to a subterranean chamber. From this descending passage another led
up to a gallery connected below with a supposedly

Queen's chamber and above with a King's chamber, placed along the main vertical axis nearly half way to the apex from the base. Two so-called ventilating shafts respectively connected the king's chamber with the north and south faces of the pyramid. The orientation of these shafts is perhaps the most interesting feature of the construction of this pyramid.

Crackpot speculations of a prophetic sort concerning the measurements of the Great Pyramid have made contemporary archaeologists somewhat shy about

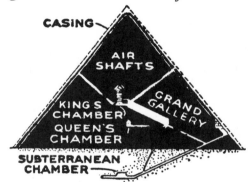

CASING

AIR SHAFTS

KING'S CHAMBER

QUEEN'S CHAMBER

GRAND GALLERY

SUBTERRANEAN CHAMBER

16. Centre section of the Great Pyramid of Khufu, Gizeh, c. 3000 B.C.

acknowledging any significance in them. By an ingenious manipulation of figures, the faithful band of Anglo-Israelites have even found fulfilment of a Biblical forecast of the triumphant entry of a British General into Jerusalem at the end of World War I, whereafter the return of God's Chosen People to Zion under the leadership of Dr. Chaim Weizmann. For such entertainments, the Chosen People have no culpable responsibility whatsoever. Their formerly Christian persecutors must take the blame.

None the less, several facts are intelligible only in terms of the indisputable calendar-keeping task of all the priesthoods of antiquity and of the equally indisputable dependence of their task on knowledge of what we nowadays call *positional* astronomy. To assess them judiciously, we should shun the temptation to draw a hard and fast line between science and magic. Nor should we insist on a clear-cut distinction between the practical and the ritual. After all, future generations may wonder why people sufficiently intelligent to measure the speed of light could regard the so-called luminiferous ether as an intelligible entity.

While it is easy for hindsight to read into the structure of the Pyramids intentions which had little or nothing to do with the preoccupations of their priestly architects, it is also unwise to assert that the precision of their construction had no intelligible end in view other than superstitions which are alien to our own habits or attention from this viewpoint. The ventilating shafts of the Great Pyramid at Gizeh claim special attention from this viewpoint. The one facing north, like the tunnel leading to the underground chamber, is about 3° below the Polar Axis as if set to greet a circumpolar star then at lower culmination, i.e. when lowest below the Celestial Pole. The shaft facing South is at right angles to the face itself and thus sloped at an angle of 78° to the Polar axis, i.e. 22° to the Celestial Equator.

According to an ancient tradition, it greeted at its transit Sirius, the brightest of all the fixed stars; and Sirius, as we know (p. 14), had a special significance in connection with the Egyptian year. It is not certain that its aperture remained open, when the facing was complete; but the light of Sirius would shine directly into the king's burial chamber during the later stages of construction, if the tradition is true. On this assumption, we can estimate when the building was complete by a not very elaborate computation which makes use of the phenomenon usually called the *Precession of the Equinoxes.*

This is the name given to a roughly 25,000 (more precisely 25,800) year cycle (p. 8), known to the astronomers of Alexandria nearly two centuries before the beginning of the Christian era. Because of it, the position of the fixed stars very slowly changes in a calculable way. According to a calculation of the writer, the declination of Sirius*, i.e. its inclination at transit to the Celestial Equator (p. 103) was 22° South about the year 2400 B.C. This is remarkably close to 2575 B.C., the latest figure cited for the age of the Great Pyramid on the basis of historical chronology, i.e. the dates of the reigning Pharaohs and their successors. It is all the more so because there are gaps in the historical record and any such figure therefore relies to some extent, albeit small, on intelligent guesswork.

Be that as it may, it will not be profitless to take a look at the Great Pyramid, and at others built in accordance with the same underlying principles, from the standpoint of what the secular advisers of the dynasty of Greek-speaking conquerors with their capital in Alexandria knew two centuries before Julius Caesar landed there and initiated the Julian Calendar on the advice of the Alexandrian astronomer Sosigenes.

In 238 B.C. the ruler Ptolemy III issued the so-called *Decree of Canopus* to replace the traditional 365-day Egyptian year by what we have come to call the Julian year of 365.25 days. Seemingly, his officials and successors did not enforce it. Whether the Alexandrian astronomers took over this figure from their priestly predecessors we do not certainly know; but we do know that the construction of the Great Pyramid could have materially aided their own observations in the search for greater precision of time reckoning.

*Today, it is about $16\frac{1}{2}°$ South.

The vast size of the pyramids is very relevant to what use the astronomer priests could have made of them. Before the time of Newton, when the vernier came into use, the only way of achieving greater accuracy was to make one's measuring instrument larger. A generation before the introduction of telescopes or microscopes of a crude sort, Tycho Brahe (A.D. 1546–1601) used for his observations of planetary motion a quadrant whose diameter was 19 feet. On this scale a degree was an interval of 4 inches; and a difference of one hundredth of a degree would be detectable by the naked eye. It should not greatly tax our credulity to suppose that the Calendar Custodians of remote antiquity had stumbled on the fact that building in a big way has therefore a pay-off.

Since the setting of the Great Pyramid is such that it faces so precisely North, South, East, and West, it necessarily provides the observer with sight lines for the positions of the noon shadow when visible (*see below*) and of the rising and setting sun at the equinoxes. This equips us with four different ways of measuring the so-called *tropical** year with great precision, if recorded sufficiently often to yield a reliable mean. The tropical year is the interval between successive vernal equinoxes (March 21) or between successive autumnal equinoxes

---

*In contradistinction to the *tropical* year we now speak of the Sirius year of the earliest Egyptian calendar as the *sidereal* year, this being the interval between which the sun retreats (as the ancients would say) back to the same position with reference to the fixed stars. Owing to Precession, as we now know, this takes about 20 minutes longer than the interval between two successive spring or autumn equinoxes and between two successive summer or winter solstices, i.e. the tropical year will have become about a day less than the same number of sidereal years after a lapse of 75 years.

(September 23), and it is also the interval between two winter solstices (December 21) when the noon shadow is longest. It does not however confer the means of making a measurement based on the summer solstice (June 21). For a reason we shall now see, this occurs during a period when the pyramid casts no noon shadow.

That it does not, is itself advantageous. In fact, it provides an opportunity for two sensitive measurements, namely intervals between consecutive dates on which the noon shadow first disappears and intervals between consecutive dates when the noon shadow reappears. The reason for this vanishing trick depends on the slope of the faces. These make an angle of 52° at the base, whence 38° to the plumb line.

By a simple formula, which we shall learn about later (Part 3), we can calculate when the noon sunbeam will make an angle of 38° to the plumb line, if we have at our disposal a star map and know our latitude. This happens at the latitude of Cairo, that of the Great Pyramid of Cheops, about February 28 and about October 14. Between these dates the shadow of the noon sun cast by the Great Pyramid will disappear. Including the winter solstice and the two equinoxes, we thus have at our disposal five different annually recurring events as a basis for an estimate of the length of the tropical year. Whether the Pyramid architects took all these facts into consideration we do not certainly know. It is extremely likely that their priestly successors knew how to make use of them. Indeed it is on record that the earliest Greek traveller to gain knowledge of elementary geometry in Egypt spent some of his time in conference with the temple astronomers boastfully devising (or more probably learning) ways of measuring the height of the Great Pyramid from the length of its shadow.

17. (a) Aerial view of
         Stonehenge

The cult of sun worship and the priestly art of impressing the laity by the forecast of eclipses spread into cloudier northern regions. There the lay-out of temple and tombs had to do the task of regulating the calendar without recourse to a written record. One example of such an architectural feat in the colder north has lately disclosed its secrets. On the lonely landscape of Salisbury Plain in southern England, stands visibly near a main motorway what is perhaps the most impressive relic of the Bronze Age north of the Alps (Figs. 17a and 17b).

Such is Stonehenge. Even in ancient times, when imposing temples were a familiar feature of the Mediterranean scene, it excited the admiration of Diodorus, a Greek-speaking Sicilian who wrote extensively on

(b) Ground view of Stonehenge

history and geography. Writing of Britain (about 40 B.C.), he could have referred to none other when he states that "there is also on the island both a magnificent sacred precinct of Apollo and notable temple". Apollo here means the Sun, and it has long been known, as is still conspicuous, that the main axis of the huge standing stones greets sunrise at the summer solstice. As the mid-summer sun first becomes visible above the skyline, one still-standing stone, called the *heel stone,* half conceals its disc as seen from the centre of its circle of pillars. That the edifice was, in effect, an observatory with a special significance for the maintenance of a calendar based on the tropical year is therefore beyond dispute. There are also good reasons to believe that its role as a repository of astronomical lore was much more comprehensive.

First, let us look at what remains today. As seen from

18. Heel Stone,
    Stonehenge

the nearest roadway across the Plain, what is most conspicuous is an outer and an inner group of standing
pillars of quadrilateral section capped above by massive
horizontal stones (*lintels*), themselves also of quadrilateral
section (Fig. 18). The outer group stand in a circle nearly
100 feet wide. The upright stones which carry the lintels
are of equal size, 18 feet long with 4 feet below the
ground. Originally, there were thirty pillars; but some
have fallen, as have lintels between adjacent pillars of the
inner group. When the outer group was complete the
lintels formed a continuous ring.

The inner group consisted originally of 5 trilithons*,
i.e. pairs of pillars supporting a single horizontal stone;
of these only two are now complete. Their disposition
recalls the shape of a horseshoe whose open end faces the
heel stone, i.e. the rising sun of midsummer day (Fig. 19).
The middle trilithon at the opposite end was higher (22
feet) than the two at the free end (about 16 feet).

Where the inner surface of the uprights and the under
surface of the lintels have not suffered exposure to the

*From the Greek for *three* as in *triangle* and for *stone* as in *Neolithic* and
lithograph, i.e. three stones.

19. Sunrise of mid-
summer day,
Stonehenge

weather, it is still evident that the edges and surfaces had been fashioned with great care and skill. The latter do not lie loosely on the former, but have peg and hole junctures. Adjacent lintels of the outer ring of pillars fitted together by tongue and groove. There is no evidence that either group of pillars and lintels ever supported a roof. It is improbable that they could have done so. There is therefore a *prima facie* reason for the supposition that they had another function.

At eye level, there are remains of other circles of smaller stones, and, from above, as we can now see so clearly by recourse to aerial photography (Fig. 20) the picture includes three rings of pits which do not seem to have been sockets for standing stones. Three of these rings are concentric with what is recognisable from the

20. Plan of the stones and
    excavated areas,
    Stonehenge

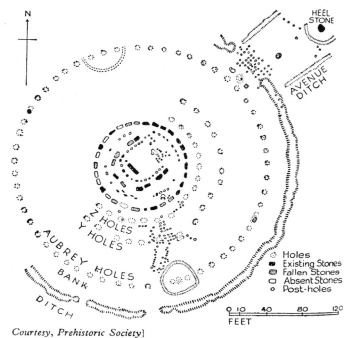

Courtesy, *Prehistoric Society*]

Plan of the stones and excavated areas

air as once a vast circular ditch. The ditch itself is concentric with the outer ring of pillars. The outermost of the rings of pits are the *Aubrey* stones, so called after an eighteenth-century antiquarian who drew attention to them. Inside and nearer the outer ring of massive pillars, are those known as the Y and Z holes (Fig. 21).

Of the Y and Z holes more anon. Their gaps are not spaced at even crudely measured equal intervals. On the other hand, the Aubrey holes are as near as may be equally spaced. Oddly enough there are 56 of them. To lay out 32 or 64 equally spaced pits by the peg and rope method (pp. 48–54) of the temple architects of antiquity would be simple to accomplish by successive bisection of 4 right angles with a common apex; but to lay out 56 pits as equally spaced as the Aubrey holes is a far more sophisticated performance. The difficulty of the under-

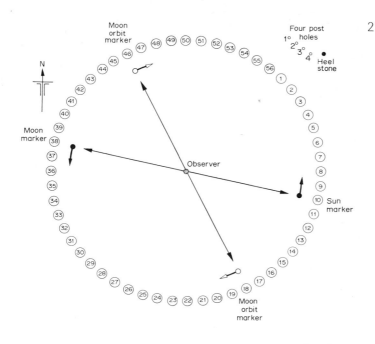

21. Aubrey holes, an eclipse clock, as interpreted by Professor Hawkins. The sun marker would need to be moved two holes anti-clockwise every 13 days to complete one circuit a year. The moon marker would be moved two holes anti-clockwise each day—one circuit each lunar month.
The moon orbit markers (or node markers), representing the points where the moon's orbit as seen from the earth intersects the sun's path through the zodiac, would be moved clockwise three holes a year—one circuit every 18.6 years.
An eclipse would take place when sun and moon markers coincided at one of these points or 'nodes'.

taking tempts us to ask what end the architects had in view.

Before we examine one answer to this question, let us take stock of recent discoveries which throw some light on who were the architects of the final structure. Geological evidence has shown that some of the stones are not of local origin. Indeed, they can have come only from the South West of Wales. If so, they must have travelled by sea most of the way to their destination. A more recent discovery adds to the interest of this fact. In the construction of the great standing pillars, some archaeologists have long since discerned indications of skills peculiar to those of the Greek conquerors of Crete at a date about 1600 B.C. In 1953, a hitherto unnoticed carving of a hilted dagger came to light. Experts have identified it as Grecian and date it at about 1600 B.C. It now seems that trade between the Mediterranean and the South West of Britain where tin is most abundant existed long before 1000 B.C., i.e. at a date very much earlier than when one used to believe that Phoenician ships and those of their Greek-speaking trade rivals first ventured north of the Straits of Gibraltar in search of tin for the manufacture of Bronze. If so, we have an answer to one enigma of Stonehenge. The changeable weather of Britain is most unpropitious to astronomical observation. Indeed, it is inconceivable that folk confined by its shores in such a climate could have constructed under their own steam a calendar based on the tropical year.

On the other hand, it is easy to believe that migrants from, or one might say missionaries of, a culture which flourished in a sunnier climate would be welcome to the Aborigines, if they brought with them the magic of a calendar to serve the purposes of a seasonal economy. In much the same way, Africans in our own century have welcomed Christian intruders whose arsenicals and antibiotics are so much more efficacious than the ministrations of the native medicine man.

From the remains of charred bones, by recourse to the Radio-Carbon Test,* it is now possible to date with confidence both who were the earliest builders of the Stonehenge remains, and when they built it in Britain. The Bronze Age there began about 2000 B.C. with arrival from the Continent of the Beaker Folk, so called because of the characteristic vessels found with their remains. In about 1600 B.C., it reached its highest level in the part of England called Wessex. This includes Salisbury Plain where Stonehenge stands. Between these limits, we can now date the construction of the great Sun Temple in three stages. The first stage occurred about 1900 B.C. It consisted of a great circular banked ditch already mentioned, with an aperture facing a boulder of local stone.

*See *Beginnings and Blunders* p. 15.

So placed, an observer at the centre of the circular ditch looking towards the gap to its north-eastern extremity would see the sun rising above it on midsummer day. Such was the *Heel Stone*, still standing. The other conspicuous standing stones belong to the third stage, when the Wessex culture was at its peak, i.e. about 1600 B.C. On the other hand, the ring of 56 Aubrey holes was part of the original plan to which the Heel Stone belongs.

Lately, researches by Professor Hawkins of the Harvard-Smithsonian Observatory have thrown new light on these 56 pits, which were never sockets for a ring of standing pillars.* His quest began by showing that the builders placed the gaps in the trilithons of the horseshoe and corresponding visible gaps in the outer continuous circle of pillars so that an observer looking outwards from the former would see sunrise and sunset at midwinter and midsummer, midwinter moonrise and moonset, likewise midsummer moonrise and moonset. Other alignments made visible the positions of moonrise and moonset on successive equinoxes at extreme limits somewhat beyond those of midsummer and midwinter sunrise or sunset.

Such extreme limits of the alignments for moonrise or moonset to the north-south axis of the outer circle and horseshoe correspond with a trivial error to their positions calculated in accordance with what we now know to be inclination of the moon's orbit to the Celestial Equator (p. 103), that is to say, roughly 5° greater than that of the sun in the Ecliptic (p. 99). Seemingly therefore, we have here a sequence of observation posts to

*Some archaeologists have ridiculed the conclusions of Professor Hawkins; but he has received strong support from the British Astronomer Professor Hoyle. For other work on the calendrical significance of British Bronze Age stone circles and stone avenues, see *Megalithic Lunar Observations* by A. Thom (1971).

keep track of the relative positions of the rising sun and moon and of their setting. Since we know that eclipses depend on the relative positions of the sun and moon, and since we also know that eclipses were events invested with dread or exultation in ancient times, the whole picture suggests that the end in view of the architects was to forecast them.

That eclipses of the moon occur only when it is full, and of the sun only when it is new, must have been a familiar fact to the priestly astronomers in remote antiquity when the number of days between successive full or new moons was a basic datum for keeping track of the seasons. A solar eclipse on midsummer day when the sun rises over the Heel Stone, and a lunar eclipse when moonrise tallies with sunrise or midwinter sunset, must have seemed very auspicious events to the architects of Stonehenge. If so, the number of Aubrey holes is highly suggestive of their intentions. Calculations, no longer prohibitively laborious where electronic computers are available, have made it possible to date all eclipses in the period 2000–1000 B.C. The outcome is that they occurred only when the midwinter moon would, like the midsummer sun, rise behind the Heel Stone.

We now know that the mean number of years between eclipses of either sort is a little over 18.6, that is almost exactly a sequence of 19, 18 and 19 years making a total of 56 years. This makes intelligible a reference by Diodorus to the visit of the god at intervals of 19 years; and it is difficult to regard as mere coincidence the fact that the number of Aubrey holes is 56. Thus by moving a single stone or post from one hole to the next once a year, it would complete an eclipse cycle of 56 years. With three stones or posts used in the same way, and spaced accordingly, it could keep track of sequences of 19, 18 and 19 years.

Such a procedure would be of no consequence unless the priestly watchers of the sky had a means of keeping track of the approach of midwinter day. We have a clue to this as well. The interval between two full moons or two new moons, being almost exactly 29.5 days, is the mean of 29 and 30 days. It happens that the number of Y holes outside the main edifice is 30 and the number of Z holes is 29. Also, though less certainly, the number of small stones in the circle between the outer pillars and inner trilithons would appear to be 59 = 30 + 29. If the latter figure is correct, moving a marker stone or wedge morning and evening from one stone to the next would complete a $29\frac{1}{2}$-day cycle. In any event, moving a stone from one to the next Y hole in the morning and one to the next Z hole in the evening (or *vice versa*) would accomplish the same result.

The architects and the Druids have left no traces of a written record, as we usually speak of such. Even if they had left no relic other than a crumbling circle whose centre is in line with the Heel Stone at midsummer sunrise, they would have bequeathed us a clue to the most compelling circumstance that made the written record necessary. Because time flies, and because keeping track of the seasons was a necessity for stocking the larder when settled life began, folk had to learn in some way or other to keep a tally of time.

What strokes, if any, the Druid priests inscribed on materials of which we have no remains we may never know. What is certain is that the architects of Stonehenge brought to a land more barbarous than their own the know-how for keeping track of the seasons by devices which other peoples with the art of writing a record of the passage of time had already mastered. That they did so, gives us one of many clues to how writing must have begun two thousand years earlier.

3 **The Legacy of the Temple**

If we use the term communication to include the use of numeral signs and mathematics as the written language of size and shape, we can recognise in the background of each stage when scientific knowledge has conspicuously leapt forward an advance of the technique of communication. Conversely, a breakdown of man's means of communication characterises a period of stagnation. It is also true that improvement in our means of communication permitting a larger literacy recruits a new reservoir of personnel and thereby enlists new resources of human experience.

A great leap forward about 500 B.C. was possible because alphabetic writing had become available to a maritime people, and a literate class of master mariners had come into being. The great leap forward we associate with the names of Thales, Pythagoras and other Greek-speaking pioneers of science in the sixth and fifth centuries B.C., was pre-eminently a marriage of astronomy and mathematics. It is therefore appropriate to complete the story of what posterity owes to the astronomer priests of Egypt and Iraq by a brief account of their writing and of their mathematical knowledge.

With the need to keep track of the passage of time by elaborating a battery of number signs, other techniques coalesced as a means of cataloguing temple property and recording auspicious events or ceremonial dates. From the start, our own species in the Old Stone Age had been picture makers, and pictures of objects, such as animals sacred to a tribe, are the likely origin of seals used as a signature—identifying the ruler who replaced the tribal chief as villages coalesced to form city communities with intercommunication by trade. Be that as it may, the scripts used both in Egypt (Fig. 22) and in Iraq during the period which concerns us here began as pictorial signs which became more or less conventionalised at an early date, i.e. before 2500 B.C. Such pictorial signs represented individual words having at first no relation to the sounds we utter.

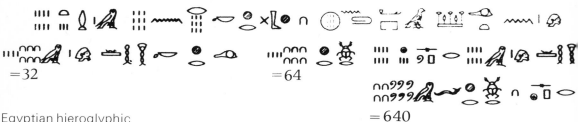

=32

=64

=640

22. Egyptian hieroglyphic writing, showing numerals

In the course of time, Egyptian scribes (Fig. 22) enlarged their battery of signs by what one may call pictorial puns which did in fact have sound values. What this means may be illustrated in English by setting the picture of a bee in front of a picture of a leaf to represent the sound of the word *belief*. However, Egyptian script never consistently became phonetic in the sense that Japanese syllable script and European alphabetic script is phonetic and, as such, call for the memorisation of a comparatively small number of signs. In short, the pupil who aspired to become a scribe in ancient Egypt had to memorise an enormous number of signs, as is still true of Chinese students. Learning to read was thus a very protracted and laborious process; and this was a formidable obstacle to the spread of literacy beyond the temple precincts.

An obstacle of a different sort obstructed the spread of literacy in the Middle East during the same period of time, i.e. before the contribution of the maritime Greeks. This was the nature of their writing materials. At an early date, i.e. before 2500 B.C., the Egyptians had learned to make, by glueing strips of a locally abundant grass, a thin

23. (a) Cuneiform
         Tablet

(b) Cuneiform script
     showing mathe-
     matical problems.
     Eighteenth
     century B.C. Old
     Babylonian

membrane (*papyrus*) on which the scribe could write with ink of a sort. Such a membrane was very flexible and like our toilet paper, easy to roll into a compact cylinder (*scroll*) which was light to hold and made no excessive demand on space. Contrariwise, our documentary records from Iraq are baked clay tablets or metal cylinders vastly more bulky than scrolls.

As the pictorial origin of the signs became less and less recognizable, there emerged in Iraq a new style of representation by wedge-like strokes, made initially by a wooden punch in the moist clay before baking. One speaks of this script as *cuneiform* (Figs. 23a and 23b). It goes without saying that any record of this sort could accommodate a sizable store of information only in very large buildings. This, rather than the difficulties of learning the arts of reading or writing, was the main obstacle to a high level of literacy.

Actually, cuneiform writing had become phonetic at a comparatively early date. It began in the region of the two great rivers Tigris and Euphrates among a priest-hood which spoke a tongue, *Sumerian,* possibly allied to Turkish but certainly not Semitic. Before 2000 B.C., an immigrant Semitic population had gained ascendancy in the same region, and had continued writing in the cunei-form style, but the symbols though visibly like those of the Sumerian period were now comparable to the Japanese syllabaries based on borrowed Chinese signs but used as symbols of sound. Possibly, the reason for the transition was the same. Pointing to a sign, the illiterate alien who spoke a foreign language would associate it with its sound though ignorant of its meaning.

From the site of one of the ziggurats (p. 19), step temples of the ancient city of Nippur in Iraq, excavation has brought to light some 50,000 clay tablets in cuneiform script composed at latest about 2000 B.C. Such is the source of what we shall later learn about the knowledge of computation in the temple libraries of Iraq. It is likely that some progress in astronomy and in mathematics continued long beyond that date and even after the great leap forward of science among Greek-speaking innovators in Alexandria about 300 B.C.

The same can scarcely be said of what Egypt bequeathed posterity. Two scrolls which have survived the ravages of time and climate, each dated about 1500 B.C. supply us with all the documentary evidence we have about Egyptian mathematics, and there is little, if any, evidence to record considerable later progress on the banks of the Nile. One such scroll, the beautifully preserved Rhind Papyrus, composed by a temple scribe known as Ahmes, is in the British Museum in London (Fig. 24). The other, called the Moscow Papyrus, is where we should guess it

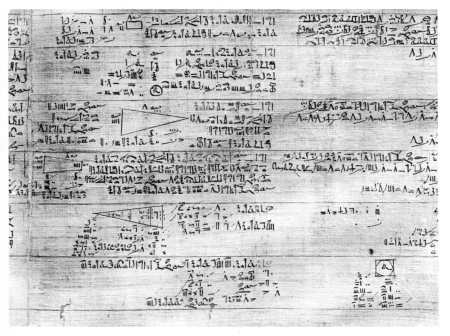

24. Rhind papyrus

to be. Neither scroll gives us any insight into whether Egyptian astronomy ever advanced greatly in theory or practice beyond its contribution to the calendar.

From the tombs of the Rameses dynasty at Thebes and at dates about 1100 B.C., excavation has unearthed texts which depict a lay-out gridwise to determine the highest altitude of particular stars at different times of the night. In short, it anticipates what we now call a graph. Possibly, the hours of this chart were of equal length based on the position of the stars in a circumpolar constellation, as some shepherds can still keep track of time at night, and as some people in the west used night dials (Fig. 5a) two or three centuries back.

Before we look at what the scrolls and tablets tell us of our debt to the temple cultures of remote antiquity, let us ask what know-how made it possible to build their enduring monuments. Direct information concerning the instruments the temple architects used is scarce, but we hear from the Greek writer Democritus (about 400 B.C.), father of the atomic view of matter, and pre-eminent as a mathematician in his own generation, that he learned much from the Egyptian "rope stretchers". That what he learned was not trivial is clear from his own declaration that:

there is no one who has surpassed me in geometric constructions and demonstrations, no not even the geometers of Egypt among whom I passed five full years of my life.

If we ask ourselves how the temple and pyramid architects got results so impressive with the means at their disposal, we here have a clue. For large scale geometrical constructions a rope stretched vertically by a weight (a *plumb line*) (Figs. 25 and 26) is the only way the architects of antiquity had of building a right angle in the vertical plane. If stretched between two pegs a rope

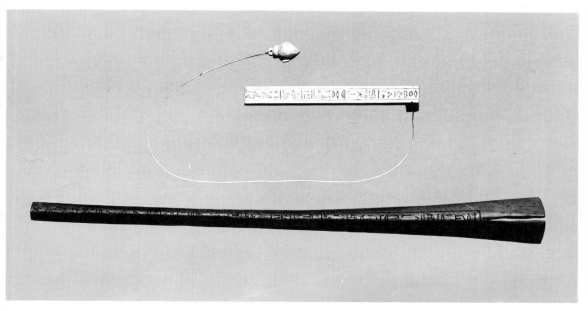

USE OF THE MERKHET IN ANCIENT EGYPT

25. Reconstruction of ancient Egyptian *merkhet*. The plumb line was an essential part of the *merkhet*, used by the Egyptian astronomer priest as a sort of sundial. Seemingly, in conjunction with an instrument called by modern scholars the *bay*, they used it when sighting rising and setting positions of stars

26. *Merkhet* and *bay* one use of the plumb line in ancient Egypt

C

can also serve as a ruler to draw a straight line on a flat surface of sand or soil. If one peg is free to rotate, leaving a dent on the latter, it will also trace out a circle. In short, it can do the work of rule and compass sacrosanct to later geometers of Plato's school.

Alike for a temple wall and the base of a pyramid, how to make a right angle on the horizontal plane was essential to the construction. We may infer that the temple architects first used the familiar Euclidian recipe rule and compass which serves also as a means of dissecting a line (Fig. 27). A second method known seemingly to the Egyptians and certainly to the temple architects of Iraq

27.

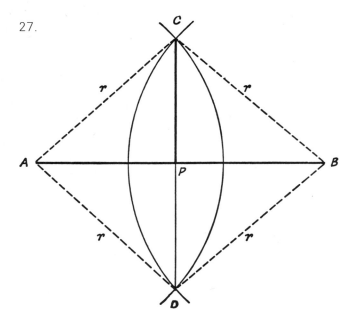

depends on a recipe for making a set square on sand or soil.

This method (Fig. 28) takes advantage of the fact that one angle of a triangle is a right angle, if the lengths of its sides are in the ratio 3:4:5, the right angle itself being the

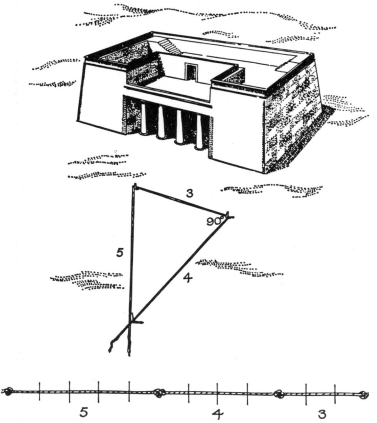

28. Speculative recon-
struction of the Set
Square of the Temple
Architects.

angle opposite the longest side. The rope stretcher could
take advantage of this rule as follows. Make 4 knots in a
cord, with their centres respectively 3, 4, and 5 lengths
of a straight bar or rod apart. Peg down on the sand or
soil the two middle knots after stretching taut the rope
between them. Then with a peg through the two end
knots, stretch each remaining segment and fix them
down.

Needless to say, the ratio 3:4:5 is an example of what
we learn at school as Pythagoras' Theorem, i.e. $a^2 + b^2 = c^2$ if c is the longest side. The temple computers of Iraq
knew many other sets of whole numbers which illustrate

the same rule, e.g. 5:12:13. They also knew another rope and peg recipe for making a right angle on the flat. This depends on the very important geometrical truth that a triangle is right angled if one of its sides is the diameter of a circle and the remaining apex is a point on its boundary.

Given a means of identifying the shortest and longest day, the orientation of a temple entrance to greet the rising sun of either solstice was a purely empirical problem; but the identification itself is a more sophisticated matter. One simple method is to make daily observations around the time when the noon shadow of a pole or pillar is longest or shortest to ascertain the date of its seasonally minimum or maximum values. Here again a rope trick (Fig. 29a) suffices to determine the direction of the noon shadow on a given day.

With cord and peg one may trace a half circle pointing northwards around the pole or pillar at a distance determined by previous observation somewhat beyond the reach of the shortest shadow of the day. The watcher must then wait until the tip of the shadow touches the circular arc successively before and after mid-day, marking each point. Bisection of the angle between the

29. (a)

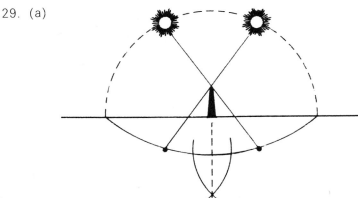

pole or pillar and these two points precisely fixes the
position of the noon shadow. The rope-trick rule for
bisection of an angle is, of course, our first rope and peg
rule for making a right angle.

In achieving this we have settled the North-South axis
of our local horizon and the rope stretcher has also pro-
vided himself with two ways of making a temple site to
greet the rising (or setting) sun of the equinoxes, i.e. the
two days when the sun actually rises and sets (as nearly
as possible) due East and due West. The East-West is at
right angles to the North-South axis which we have
disposed of. Hence the rope and peg (3:4:5) set square
suffices to fix it.

This may seem to be the simplest, but not necessarily
the earliest, way of solving the problem. Alternatively,
with less geometrical know-how, those of an earlier
vintage than the pyramid architects may have adopted
what was intuitively, though not obviously at first sight
a more direct, approach. Having sited empirically by a
suitable monument the rising sun of the longest and
shortest days, the temple architect or surveyor could fix
that of the equinoxes to a high level of precision by
bisecting the angle between them (Fig. 29b).

Architecture was not the only pace-maker for geometrical rule of thumb in the dawn of science; the word
itself based on Greek literally means *earth measurement*.
A Greek-speaking Iraq emigré, from whom we get our
not wholly reliable first glimpses of contemporary
civilisation in the Mediterranean world of antiquity,
asserts that geometry had its origin in the task of the
Egyptian income tax collectors who levied temple tribute
on the basis of allotment acreage. At a time when the
annual flooding of the Nile might wash away landmarks
which bounded allotments of the tillers of the soil,

29(b)

frequent measurements of this sort were necessary (Fig. 30).

What we certainly know from scrolls of papyrus which have withstood the hazards of the weather is that the temple computers of the Nile could calculate correctly areas of rectangles and right-angled triangles. Curiously, the rule given for the latter is to divide by two the product of the lengths of the two shortest sides. For instance for the 3:4:5 triangle $\frac{1}{2}(3 \times 4) = 6$. From the same scroll

30. Fifteenth century B.C. Egyptian surveying, from a wall painting

(the Rhind papyrus), we learn that the value of π, the ratio of the area to the square of the radius of a circle is, in our way of writing down numbers, 3.16. This is remarkably close to the true value 3.142 (to three decimal places, an error of approximately 2 in 300, i.e. less than one per cent).

A good value for π had a pay-off in terms of temple tribute, because a cylinder open at one end is a convenient shape for a container in which to measure grain, oil, or wine. An achievement in measurement of volume recorded in the papyrus now in Moscow is more remarkable and less obviously—if at all—useful. Before the completion of Stonehenge, the Egyptian temple computers could correctly calculate the volume of a whole or truncated pyramid.

When measuring height levels in sunny climates, where skies are mostly cloudless, information from oriental sources suggests that the architects of ancient times made much use of the sun's shadow. Tradition tells us that Thales, the earliest of the Greek geometers on record, determined the height of the Great Pyramid of Gizeh (Fig. 31) for the instruction of his priestly hosts. To do so, we need to know only the basic principle of trigonometry, i.e. that the ratios of the corresponding sides of similar right-angled triangles are equivalent. One measures the length of the noon shadow of a pole of known height, and that of the Pyramid added to half the width of its base. It is at least as likely that his priestly instructors taught Thales the trick as that he made the discovery.

In the domain of practical mensuration, the Egyptian temple teachers were in some ways in advance of their opposite numbers in Iraq. The latter clung, like the Hebrews in the Old Testament (I Kings VII, 23), to the value 3.0 for π. Contrariwise, the art of computation, as we learn from the Nippur tablets, reached a much higher level in the Middle East than in Egypt.

In Iraq, there was a more powerful impetus to calculation than in the Egypt of the Moscow papyrus (about 1600 B.C.). In Egypt, the priestly hierarchy with its associated scribes, architects, engineers, and surveyors preyed on a vast population of slave labour in the fields and the mines. The cities of Iraq were more lively centres of overland trade routes and a large class of freemen in-

31. One way in which Thales may have measured the height of the Great Pyramid at Gizeh by measuring the length of the noon shadow:

$$H \div (\tfrac{1}{2}b + S) = \tan A = p \div s$$
$$\therefore H = p(\tfrac{1}{2}b + S) \div s$$

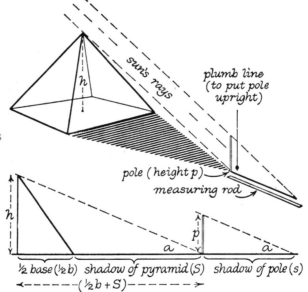

sun's rays

plumb line (to put pole upright)

pole (height p)
measuring rod

h

p

a a

½ base (½ b) shadow of pyramid (S) shadow of pole (s)
$\longleftarrow ------(\tfrac{1}{2}b+S)----- \longrightarrow$

cluded bankers as well as merchants and pedlars. There was an elaborate code of weights and measures and customs concerning wages. Commercial arithmetic flourished accordingly. For instance, one cuneiform record gives a recipe for computing compound interest at 20% over a specified period of time.

Without going into further details, two features of the art of computation as it flourished in Iraq are of special interest in terms of what it eventually bequeathed to posterity. Of these, their system of dealing with fractions, which were a nightmare to the Egyptian computers, still survives in our method of measuring angles and time. This is the so-called sexagesimal system in which fractions are expressed as the sum of terms of the form:

$$\frac{a}{60} + \frac{b}{60^2} \text{ etc.}$$

The use of the base 60 embraced the representation of large integers in astronomical records. That is to say symbols for 60, 60^2, 60^3, take the place of I, X, C, and M of the Roman numerals. This was a great economy of space for a script which preserved the principle of repetition (p. 16). In dealing with fractions the base has one great advantage over 10 whose only factors are 2 and 5. The factors of 60 are 2, 3, 4, 5, 6, 10, 12, 15, and 30.

Before we turn to another remarkable feature of

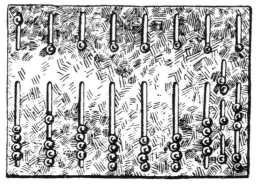

32. The Abacus
    (a) Roman

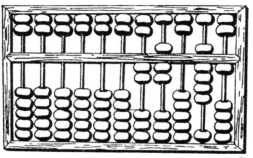

(b) Chinese

(c) Japanese

computation revealed by the Nippur tablets, let us look at the way in which a temple scribe in Egypt would perform addition and multiplication. To do this he would rely on a device of great antiquity. At a later date, it became a flat board (Roman type) on which beads were free to move in parallel grooves, or a frame (Japanese and Chinese types) in which perforated beads moved freely on parallel rods (Fig. 32).

At a more primitive level in Egypt, such a device (called an *abacus*) was probably a tray sprinkled with a thick layer of sand in which parallel grooves accommodated ten pebbles. Actually, the Latin word for a pebble is *calculus*, whence *calculation*. To count out 527 pebbles, the computer would start with all grooves empty, placing 9 in the first groove (for *units*). He would then empty it, placing one of the remaining pebbles on the next groove (for *tens*). When he had placed 9 on the second groove, he would empty it and place one of the remaining pebbles on the third groove (for *hundreds*). Proceeding in this way, he would end by having 7 on the first, 2 in the second, and 5 on the third groove. In his own script he would record the result (in reverse order to Roman DXXVII) as:

$$\begin{matrix} \text{III} & & \mathbf{99} \\ \text{IIII} & \text{nn} & \mathbf{999} \end{matrix}$$

To add 716 to 527, the computer would start with the final set of 7, 2, and 5 pebbles on the first three grooves and count out 716 in the same way. Multiplication being repeated addition (and division being repeated subtraction) need not trouble us. What we have seen suffices to show that the Egyptian temple scribe did not use number signs in the way we use them as counters for calculation. He used them only as a device for recording an operation performed with a mechanical device. As for

most of the world before the Hindu-Arabic script came
into general use and made possible *carrying over* on paper
without mechanical aids, they were merely labels for an
operation performed on the abacus. The latter became
redundant when the Hindus hit upon a symbol (zero) for
the empty column.

Unlike their successors for several millennia thereafter,
the computers of Iraq relied on tables which they used as
we now use tables of trigonometrical ratios or of
logarithms, and as a ship's captain uses tables of the
position of stars. A temple library could accommodate
thousands of clay tablets on which columns of numbers
had been inscribed; but the equipment for performing
a wide range of calculation would be vastly too bulky
for a ship's cargo to accommodate. The literacy, or might
we say the *numeracy,* of Iraq was still largely circumscribed by the temple walls.

Tables constructed in Iraq before 2000 B.C. include
reciprocals for dealing with division, multiplication,
squares, and cubes, as well as square roots and cube
roots. According to Dr. Neugebauer, a value assigned to
$\sqrt{2}$ is equivalent in our notation to 1.414213 instead of
1.414214 . . . , i.e. correct to six significant figures, an
error of 1 in a million. Tablets show that computers used
such tables for solving by numerical approximation
simple quadratic, and even some types of cubic,
equations.

4 **The Greek Contribution**

From even earlier than the beginning of the second millennium before the Christian era, i.e. 2000 B.C. (Fig. 33) the Mediterranean had already become a centre of maritime trade and colonisation by two widely different speech communities which founded trading posts along its shores. One eventually founded colonies along the African coast as far as Spain. Its homeland was what we now call Lebanon, the Phoenicia of the Christo-Judaic scriptures. Its language was one of the Semitic dialects akin to Hebrew and to the dominant speech of the people of Iraq during the same period.

33. Egyptian sea-going
     ship (*c.* 2600 B.C.)

From waves of invaders north of modern Greece, and speaking different Greek dialects, the other spread out first to Asia Minor in the neighbourhood of the Dardanelles, i.e., the region where the Trojan wars took place. Thence they founded trading colonies along the coast of what is now Turkey in Asia, and annexed Crete which was then the seat of a flourishing temple culture comparable with that of contemporary Egypt and Iraq. They also occupied Cyprus, Sicily and the toe of Italy. Later they founded a mercantile colony at what we now call Marseilles.

34. Phoenician warship

Phoenician trade between Lebanon and Egypt had begun before their ships set up trading stations further afield (Figs. 34 and 35). The main export from the latter was then the much-prized cedar wood of the former. The traders themselves are relevant to how science began for two reasons. One is that they were probably the first to sail beyond the Pillars of Hercules, i.e. the Straits of Gibraltar, coasting north to Britain in search of tin and along the African coast in search of spices, ivory, and black slaves. From what we now know about the so-called Wessex culture of which the Stonehenge Sun Temple is a relic, it now seems certain that Greek-speaking pilots from Crete also penetrated the Atlantic before 1500 B.C. By doing so they and their rivals brought within the range of human experience an entirely new picture of the firmament.

35. Phoenician bracelet

The date last mentioned puts the spotlight on a second fact of relevance to our story. Somewhere later than 2000 B.C. but not later than 1500 B.C., Semitic slaves in the mines of the Sinai peninsula began to adapt a small battery of Egyptian hieroglyphics to represent the sounds of a tongue alien to that of their masters and overseers. Such was the first alphabet, as some experts maintain, and the parent of all truly alphabetic writing. Be that as it may, the Semitic Phoenicians were using an alphabet (Fig. 36) of consonant signs for inscription on stone or clay tablets at a date not much later than their first foray beyond the Mediterranean, and it is certain that their trading stations were the route by which alphabetic writing first spread throughout the Mediterranean region.

36.   Phoenician script

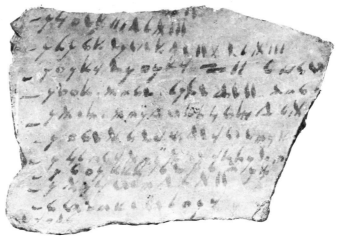

The Phoenicians did not, like their Greek pupils, perfect it as an instrument of scientific communication or as a gateway to wider literacy. To why they failed one cannot give a complete answer; but two reasons are relevant. One is that they continued for the greater part of their history, if not till the end, to use tablets of the sort used by their neighbours throughout the Middle East. Another is that they were the most priest-ridden people of the ancient world. Wherever the Phoenicians set up colonies they established the cult of Baal-Ammon, the Moloch of the Old Testament. They propitiated him with human sacrifice, that of young children, on a scale which no other civilisation has ever practised.

Both in Crete and in Cyprus, their Greek-speaking trade rivals had learned to use alternative forms of syllabic writing comparable to the *kana* syllabaries of the Japanese. Such writing meets the need of people whose words are strings of simple syllables made up of a vowel or a vowel preceded by a simple consonant, e.g. TO-KI-O, O-SA-KA, KO-BE, YO-KO-HA-MA. Syllabic writing is however a very clumsy and unreliable method of conveying the sounds of words in an Indo-European language such as Greek or our own which embraces thousands of different syllables, some closed by a consonant or consonant cluster, as in our words *strips* and *plants*, at both ends.

In languages other than those of the Semitic group, we may make many words with no common thread of meaning with the same framework of consonants in a fixed order, e.g. *man, moon, mine, moan, mean* in English. This is not true of languages of the group used by the Phoenicians. An alphabet of consonant signs suffices for identification of a Semitic word because every root with a particular meaning is a unique permutation of consonants. To make the consonant alphabet suitable to their own needs, Greek-speaking traders and master mariners had to incorporate vowel signs borrowed from one or other of syllabaries they had previously used. This happened at some date a little before 600 B.C.; and it is significant that the colonising Greek-speaking trade rivals of the Phoenicians had by then, or earlier, acquired the use of papyrus scrolls from their Egyptian customers. This date therefore pinpoints what proved to be a momentous expansion of literacy and the beginnings of what we may rightly call the Greek contribution to science.

When some writers on the dawn of science write about the Greek contribution, it is doubly misleading to ourselves. So we must be clear what we shall henceforth mean by it. When we speak of Greeks nowadays, we usually mean people who live on the mainland of Greece together, it may be, with the inhabitants of Crete and some of the inhabitants of Cyprus. In fact, the Greek-speaking world of the first millennium and especially of the last two centuries before the Christian era covered a much larger territory. Before 400 B.C. it extended from Asia Minor to Spain. For several centuries after 300 B.C. it also included parts of Egypt and the Middle East.

The different city states and colonies in the earlier period were often at war and never under a single government except during a period of less than half a century when Philip of Macedon and his son Alexander the Great brought them to heel and spread the use of the Greek language as a medium of cultural communication into Africa, Palestine, and Iraq. To speak of the Greek contribution to science, when one means the contribution to science of people who spoke Greek is therefore on all fours with talking about the English contribution to science embracing all the work of learned professions of England, Scotland, the United States, Canada, Australia, New Zealand and India (where English is still the chief medium of higher education) from the reign of Elizabeth I to our own time. There is, however, another reason why it is misleading to speak of the Greek contribution in connection with the progress of science over the whole period between 600 B.C. and 400 A.D., when monastic fanaticism uprooted pagan science.

The three centuries from 600 to 300 B.C. registered an

37. (a) Greek sea-going
vessel, vase
painting

(b) Greek galley

outburst of scientific curiosity and discovery which
began in the maritime colonies and had virtually come
to a standstill, by the latter date, in Athens on the mainland. Thereafter, our scene shifts to the cosmopolitan
city of Alexandria, where a new outlook and a new
programme under the impact of new cultural influences
initiated a flowering of inventive genius unparalleled
till Tudor times in our own era. This efflorescence will

be the theme of the next volume of *The Beginnings of Science*. We shall speak of it as the Alexandrian Culture. When, as here, we speak of the Greek contribution to science, our concern will be only with the period when Greek was its medium of communication but what we may rightly call the University of Alexandria had not as yet come into being.

Unlike the priest-ridden Phoenicians, the colonising Greek traders (Figs. 37a and 37b) of the Mediterranean had no native roots in the temple civilisations of the Middle East. They adopted the cults of the territories they settled in with speculative tolerance, sceptical about their cruder superstitions, curious about their material achievements, and eager to adopt what know-how could be useful to them. They were a litigious people. As such they delighted in public debates. The traveller who brought back novel information had to be ready to justify his claims. If so, he could hope to gather a group of disciples who would honour him as a teacher.

A key to this expansion of educational activity is the acquisition of the new means of communication already mentioned, an alphabet which imposed vastly less load on the memory of the learner than did the more ancient scripts. In this setting, a survival of their tribal past helped Greek-speaking peoples to make their language a peculiarly powerful medium for scientific communication. As Professor Thomson* has taught us, they institutional-ised as live drama the ritual dance and chorus of their ancestral tribes (Fig. 38).

In writing, the earliest trace of this dates from the tragedies of a Sicilian Greek, Aeschylus, born about 525 B.C. in the dawn of Greek science. Thenceforth, Athens, to which he migrated, became the home of a drama the

*Author of *Aeschylus and Athens*.

38. Early Greek drama, wall painting

works of whose authors, such as Sophocles, Euripides and Aristophanes have survived till today. Thus came to birth a unique phenomenon, a secular literature which conveys the spoken word. Alphabetic writing was no longer restricted, as hitherto it had been, to short inscriptions, diplomatic messages and records.

The Athenian drama had another consequence favourable to an expansion of literacy without parallel in the past. Its dialogue set the pattern for philosophical debate. Much of this was futile; but it served the purpose for conveying in every-day language reasons for belief and doubt.

What makes too many books about the history of science more boring than need be are catalogues of ancient worthies with their birth dates, hobbies, the more silly things they said, with little or no mention of anything useful they discovered. If a few names here follow, with dates at which such persons were middle-aged and still active, it is because what little we know about such writers is our only source of information about science in their time. Where they were born is more important than when they were born, if we are to understand what they contributed to scientific geography.

Thales, born about 650 B.C. died about 525 B.C. He was a native of Melitus, a Greek colony on the western seaboard of Asia Minor. Pythagoras, who flourished about 540 B.C. was born in Samos, a Greek island colony nearby. Anaxagoras, born like Thales in Asia Minor, flourished about a century after Pythagoras, i.e. *circa* 450 B.C. Empedocles, born in Sicily, and Leucippus, born like Thales in Miletus, flourished about the same time as Anaxagoras. Democritus, who developed some of the ideas of Leucippus was born near the Dardanelles in 460 B.C. and wrote prolifically till his death at a great age in 370 B.C.

Of all this list, Democritus alone was born on what we may then call the Greek mainland. All the others were born in outposts of maritime trade. Three at least, Thales, Pythagoras and Democritus, travelled widely, certainly in Egypt and probably in the Middle East, where they probed the secrets of temple lore. As we have seen (p. 48) Democritus acknowledged his debt to the priests of Egypt.

In one way or another, the pioneers of Greek science had unique opportunities to exploit and extend the legacy of the temple. What is more important in connexion with the most influential advances in scientific knowledge between 600 and 300 B.C., is that all of them had ample opportunities to benefit from the practical experience of the pilots engaged in sea trade. Of their debt to the priestly astronomers of the past, it is noteworthy that Thales and Anaxagoras impressed their contemporaries by their ability to forecast eclipses. Thales forecast an eclipse of the sun in 585 B.C. He seems to have conceived the earth as a flat circular disc, a belief probably current among the astronomer priests of Iraq, and consistent with the appearance of the earth's shadow in a total eclipse of the moon. Contrariwise, Pythagoras taught that the earth is spherical and that the apparent movements of the sun, moon and planets are independent of one another and of the fixed stars.

That he had good ground for his teaching, we shall see later. When we reach the generation for which Democritus wrote in his old age, we may say that belief in the sphericity of the earth had been widely accepted by the Greek intelligentsia. In the domain of astronomy, two further contributions call for comment. Anaxagoras who brought to Athens *Ionian* science, i.e. science from the Greek colonies of the eastern seaboard, astonished the court of its ruler Pericles with the announcement that the sun is a mass of blazing matter even larger than the Greek mainland. Empedocles seems to have been first to teach that the moon shines by reflected light, an interpretation correctly supported by its dark side seen in a total eclipse of the sun.

Our main concern in the next chapter will be with the enduring contribution of the Ionian pioneers of science to their Alexandrian successors. This was the marriage of mathematics with astronomy and geography. We may first recall what Thales, Pythagoras and Democritus added to the lessons they had learned from their priestly instructors during their visits to Egypt. Their temple teachers were content to record empirical rules of measurement and to illustrate them with particular examples. They never reached the stage of asking: in what circumstances or between what limits is such and such a rule reliable?

Accustomed to justify their travellers' tales in public debate, Greek mathematicians from Thales onwards introduced an entirely novel procedure, which we may properly call a demonstration. By the time of Democritus, the need for what we now know as a general proof was taken for granted. Indeed, by the time of the death of Pythagoras, the only theorems* essential to elementary trigonometry were already established on a firm basis.

Before the time of Democritus, Athens had become the main centre of intellectual debate in the Greek-speaking world. In so far as it was the home of Greek drama in its most creative period, Athens did intellectually make a contribution to science by making the written word a lively medium for human communication. As already stated we may regard it as the parent of the dialogue form in which writers on scientific topics could state a case for their conclusions. Before we ask what other influence, good or bad, Athens had on the growth of science, a diversion is due to anticipate how the influence of the two leading Athenian schools set back the clock by rejecting both a fruitful hypothesis and neglecting the sound evidence in support of it.

History records only two outstanding examples of experimental science to the credit of the Greek contribution in the sense we here use the term. Pythagoras and his followers experimented with the length of cords which make a scale on a stringed instrument. That he or they gave the correct ratios, we commemorate when text books of algebra speak of a harmonical progression. Of much greater importance is how Empedocles was

*(i)   The three angles of a triangle are equal to two right angles
  (ii) the angles at the base of an isosceles triangle are equal
  (iii) the ratios of corresponding sides of similar triangles are equal
  (iv) $a^2 + b^2 = c^2$, if c is the longest side of a right angled triangle
  (v)   the angle in a semicircle is a right angle.

39. Cast of water clock from Karnak.
A hole in the bottom lets out the water. The passage of time is indicated by the level of water. Dots marking the time are closer together at the top

the first to distinguish clearly between air and empty space, whence to show that air is a state of matter. Two thousand years elapsed before scientific discovery came once more to grips with the fact that air has weight, that it is therefore a form of highly compressible matter, and that its properties are intelligible on only one assumption loosely called the atomic, more properly the particulate, theory of matter.

To demonstrate that air has weight, Empedocles used the conical metal cylinder of a water clock (Fig. 39). This container had at the tip of the cone a small hole. Covering the opposite broad end was a strainer with fine perforations. One filled the container, states Professor Farrington, "by thrusting the broad end under water; it was put into use by inverting it and letting the water escape through the small hole at the tip of the cone". Professor Farrington describes as follows two experiments by which Empedocles "demonstrated the corporeal nature of air":

In the first, the broad end . . . was thrust under water in the usual way, but a finger was kept tight over the hole at the top of the cone. No water entered since the enclosed air could not escape. In the second demonstration, the clock was filled in the usual way, the opening in the top was closed and it was lifted out of the water without being reversed . . . no water could escape owing to the pressure of the atmosphere outside. Later experimenters reinforced this demonstration . . . by inflating bladders and exhibiting their resistance to compression.

That air has weight and that it is so highly compressible is readily intelligible on only one assumption, namely that it consists of particles far less tightly packed in the void than those of a liquid or solid. Leucippus was the first on record to formulate this explanation explicitly. Democritus, who marshalled other arguments in favour of the particulate nature of matter, conceived the particles in violent motion on less convincing evidence, albeit anticipating what we now call the kinetic theory of gases.

Epicurus, who founded a school on the island of Lesbos off the coast of Asia Minor and transferred it to Athens in 306 B.C. after the death of Aristotle, adopted the views of Democritus; but his interest in them was due less to his grasp of scientific evidence than because he regarded them as favourable to his own views on ethics. Partly perhaps because of the immense prestige of Aristotle and his school, the particulate view of matter ceased to have any influence on the progress of science till the translation of commentaries of Epicurus at the beginning of the seventeenth century of our own era in the context of Galileo's own demonstration that air has weight.

As the end of the Greek contribution comes within sight, the two major schools of Athens were the Academy

40. Masters and pupils at an Athenian school

(Fig. 40) founded by Plato in 387 A.D. and the Lyceum founded by Aristotle in 335 B.C. The Academy was the name of a park and sports ground in an Athenian suburb, where a self-governing student body shared to some extent a communal life. For twenty years before Plato's death (347 B.C.) Aristotle was one of his students. Thereafter he spent twelve years abroad, first in Asia Minor, then at the Court of Philip of Macedon as tutor to his heir who was destined to be Alexander the Great.

Plato's own teaching was hostile to the scientific curiosity of the maritime Greeks. He roundly derided astronomers who made measurements, as when he declares:

Do you not think that the genuine astronomer will . . . regard the heaven itself as framed by the heavenly architect? . . . But as to the proportion of which the day bears to the night, both to the month, the month to the year and the other stars to the sun and the moon and to one another . . . will he not hold it absurd to bestow extraordinary pains to apprehend their true relations . . . we shall let the heavenly bodies alone, if it is our design to become really acquainted with astronomy.

Few people have written more rubbish about the world than Plato in the *Timaeus*. In this engaging text book, the four elements of antiquity—earth, air, fire, and water—had each a heavenly image expressed in geometrical form based on triangles. Though some pure mathematicians rhapsodise about Plato's concern for proof, he certainly did both mathematics and natural science a disservice by driving measurements out of geometry.

In case the last remarks are obscure to the reader, a simple example will make them clear. We now learn at school that the area of a circle is given by the formula πr^2 or, if we express it in terms of the diameter ($d=2r$), as $\frac{1}{4}\pi d^2$ in which π is approximately 3.1416. It follows that the ratio of the areas of two circles whose diameters are d, and d_2 is $d_1{}^2 : d_2{}^2$. Like Euclid who transmitted Plato's geometry to posterity, the respectful pupil brought up in the Academy of Professor Plato would be content to state: *circles are to circles as are the squares on their diameters*. Area (being mensuration) and as such, a dirty word, does not enter into the prescribed form of statement. What is more, the prescribed statement contains no reference to π and is therefore utterly useless as a recipe for estimating the area of a circle.

A just verdict on Aristotle's influence cannot be so sweeping. Until the invention of the microscope at the beginning of the seventeenth century of the Christian era revolutionised man's knowledge of the reproductive process, no treatise on the comparative anatomy of animals was more comprehensive or more reliable. Much of its contents was in all probability based on first-hand studies and owed much to the travels of its author. Theophrastus, his pupil and successor, as head of the Lyceum when Aristotle himself died in 322 B.C., compiled the first known treatise cataloguing plants with alleged medicinal properties.

In terms of natural science, the major positive outcome of the Greek episode (600–300 B.C.) was the certainty that the earth is a spherical body, that astronomical and climatic consequences follow from the geometry of the sphere, whence a firm foundation for scientific geography. So much is largely our debt to the maritime colonial Greeks before Athens attracted playboy plutocrats in love with long words—and with one another. However, it is doubtful whether Aristotle's own treatise on geography adds much to the knowledge garnered by the maritime pioneers of Greek science and available in the time of Democritus. At least one may say that it did not hold back scientific enquiry.

Unfortunately, Aristotle's influence on the studies we now call physics was wholly harmful. He lent the weight of his authority to some of the silliest speculations of his predecessors, such as the notion that fire is an element and that what we now call vapours and gases are spiritual entities which rise in search of their heavenly home instead of falling. Accordingly, he rejected both the experimental evidence for a third state of matter and the fruitful hypotheses which the materialist school of Leucippus, Democritus and their followers had advanced to account for its existence. Till Galileo established the truth about terrestrial gravitation more than two thousand years later his weighty influence also handicapped experiment and fruitful speculation about how things fall freely in space.

5 **The Ancient Mariner**

So long as astronomy remained within the strait-jacket of the temple site, its only pay-off in the world's work was the regulation of a calendar suitable to the seasonal economy of the soil. Otherwise, its main driving force was to increase the power and prestige of the priesthood by successful interpretation of happy or calamitous portents which the laity witnessed with superstitious awe. Doubtless the astronomer priest deceived himself in the process of deceiving others, as happens in a Presidential election in the U.S.A., or a Parliamentary election in contemporary Britain. Be that as it may, his material situation also imposed a formidable limitation to progress. His local horizon circumscribed his awareness of, and opportunities for, studying the heavens.

The appearance on the stage of history of a new social personnel of literate merchants who were also master mariners announces both a new impetus to study the heavens and entirely novel opportunities for doing so. Greek historians do not record any writings Thales left behind. So we do not certainly know whether he was literate in the Cypriotic syllabary (p. 63), which has left a jar inscribed with his name, or in the newly introduced amenity of alphabetic writing. They attest that he was a prosperous merchant and seemingly a skilled pilot. Indeed, tradition credits him with a method of sighting the distance of a ship at sea and with a recipe for navigation of a sort he might have learned from the Phoenicians but certainly not from his priestly instructors in Egypt. If we are to believe it, he taught his apprentices how to steer a northerly course by using the stars of the Great Bear to locate the Celestial Pole (p. 8).

Early Greek writers bolstered their belief in the spherical shape of the earth by fanciful arguments; but one very sound argument advanced by Aristotle, namely the

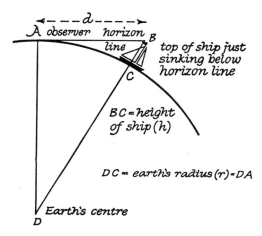

41. The visible limits of
the horizon

changing face of the heavens as the mariner steers a
northerly or southerly course, was already familar to
them. Apart from this, there was another circumstance
(Fig. 41) which must have forced itself on those engaged
in maritime trade. As a ship came within sight of port,
the pilot would see the top of a high building or monument before the base came in sight. As it left port with a
new cargo, the watcher on land would see its deck disappear before he lost sight of the mast.

Neither the experience of the pilot nor that of the
watcher is thus consistent with the belief that the earth
is flat. Aristotle's most compelling argument may well
have been one with which the pupils of Democritus were
familiar. Two great navigations of antiquity on record
supply the factual data. A little before the reported date
of the birth of Thales, a Phoenician ship commissioned by
the Egyptian ruler Necho circumnavigated Africa. It is
true that the Greek-speaking historian who recorded this

alleged event did so more than two centuries after the date at which it supposedly occurred; and the tale would therefore be easy to laugh off, if we had not one good reason to confirm our confidence in his truthfulness on this occasion. His statement that the seamen came to a region where the sun's noon shadow changes its direction records an authentic occurrence altogether outside the ken of their predecessors and of the astronomer priest.

A more reliably recorded colonial expedition of antiquity is that of Hanno (500 B.C.) along the coast of West Africa from the Phoenician city state of Carthage. Before we retrace the course, let us familiarise ourselves with what mariners could have learned from carrying cargoes within the Mediterranean before any ship had sailed past the Straits of Gibraltar and returned to port in safety. For a reason already mentioned (p. 29) the appearance of the night sky was not precisely as it is today; but we can recapture what lessons they could learn if we look at it as we might do so on a twentieth-century pleasure cruise. So we may well therefore forget about the difference and pinpoint our course by contemporary names of ports not necessarily habitable or hospitable in 2000 B.C. when maritime trade already flourished within the Mediterranean.

We must here remind ourselves that there will be no familiar landmarks on the horizon during the greater part of our voyage. We can therefore rely no longer, as did our nomadic ancestors or their astronomer priest successors, on the rising and setting positions of celestial bodies at the rim of the sky on a familiar horizon. On the other hand, it will be our privilege to make three sorts of observations our predecessors did not make by staying at home in a temple or by seeking shelter in the mouth of a cave. To make clear what these are, let us make use of some terms which we shall henceforth have to use often.

One is *transit*. This means the moment at which a heavenly body has reached the highest point in its apparently curved course across the sky. Another is *zenith*. This means an immeasurably distant imaginary point in the sky, reached by continuing the direction of the plumb line upwards. More briefly, it is a point directly overhead. When we shall speak of the *zenith distance** (z.d.) of a heavenly body, we shall here mean the angle the starbeam, moonbeam or sunbeam makes with the plumb line *at transit*. The *altitude* (*a*) of a heavenly body is its elevation at transit above the horizon. Since the plumb line is at right angles to the horizon plane, the zenith distance and altitude are related by simple formulae $z.d. = 90° - a$ and $a = 90° - z.d.$ Thus the zenith distance of a star which just grazes the horizon at transit is nearly 90° and its altitude is nearly zero.

We have already met with the terms *Celestial Pole* (p. 8) and *Circumpolar* stars or star clusters. When one speaks of the latter as at *lower culmination,* one refers to the time of the year when it dips nearest the horizon plane below. Let us now take in our stride two other technical terms. One speaks of the line on which the sun's noon shadow rests as the *Terrestrial Meridian* and one defines the *Celestial Meridian* as an imaginary semicircle passing through the Celestial Pole and the Zenith in the same plane as the terrestrial meridian. We shall speak of a star as a zenith star at a particular place, if its z.d. there is 90°, i.e. if seen directly overhead at transit at some time of the year at night.

With these definitions behind us, let us start our

---

*More pedantically, if we refer only to z.d. at transit, one should refer to it as *meridian* zenith distance.

For stars mentioned in our contemporary pleasure cruise
along the sea lanes of the great voyages of antiquity, the reader
should refer again and again to the star maps (pp. 2–5) of Chapter 1

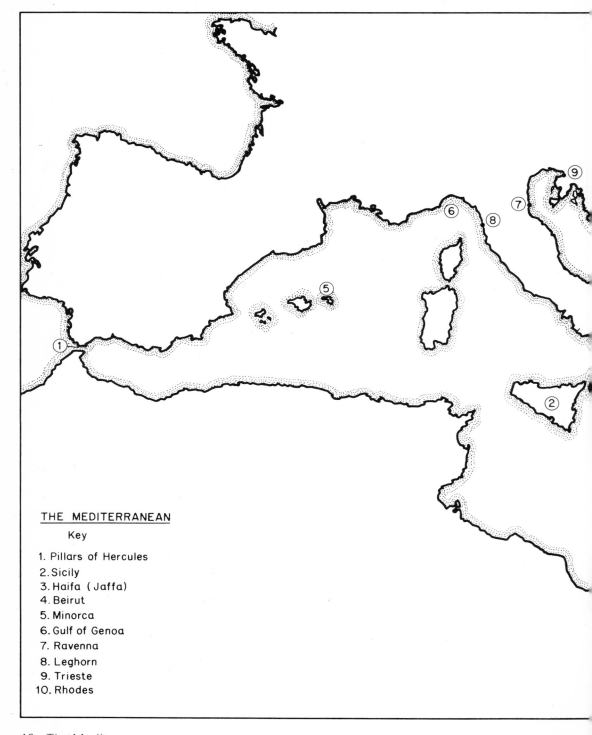

THE MEDITERRANEAN

Key

1. Pillars of Hercules
2. Sicily
3. Haifa (Jaffa)
4. Beirut
5. Minorca
6. Gulf of Genoa
7. Ravenna
8. Leghorn
9. Trieste
10. Rhodes

42. The Mediterranean

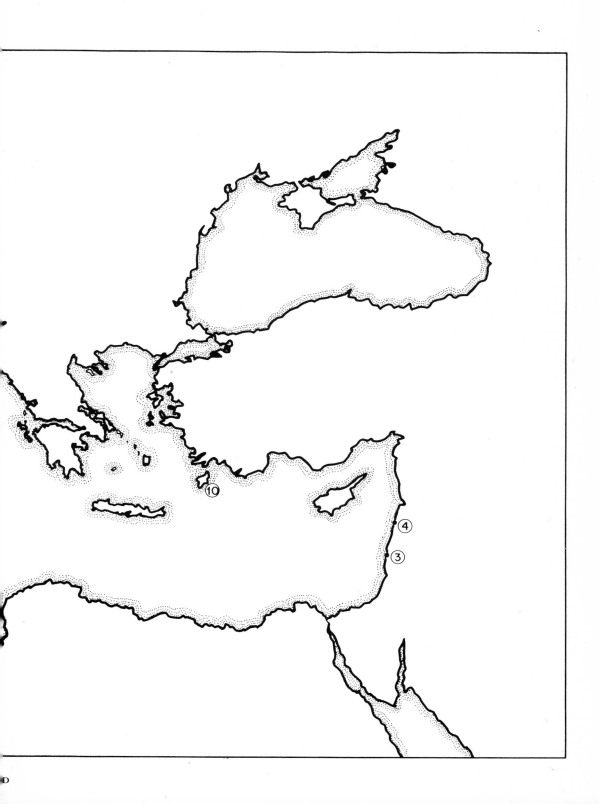

voyages under modern skies, now ready to recognise what, alas, we cannot feel the thrill of being first to view. With the advantage of hindsight, we can then anticipate three changes of the aspect of the heavens novel to the first seamen who dared to penetrate an uncharted ocean to steer their courses north or south along unfamiliar Atlantic coasts. They would see some stars become circumpolar or cease to be. They would see some stars cease to be visible at any time in the year, and see stars never hitherto visible at some time in the year come into view. They would also see some stars becoming, or ceasing to be, zenith stars, others starting or ceasing to graze the horizon.

In what follows, the reader must at all times remember that some events will be visible at some parts of the year, other events at a different part of the year. In short, master mariners of the ancient world would witness a different aspect of the sky on different cruises. Putting ourselves in their place, we shall already hold a few clues they had picked up before they set their courses beyond the confines of the great inland Mediterranean Sea, (Fig. 42). With no prevision of what we should encounter when we dared greatly beyond the Pillars of Hercules (Straits of Gibraltar), we shall have learned a few salutary lessons which we could not have picked up from our priestly tutors in Egypt or Iraq.

Most remarkable of these is the disappearance of Canopus, next to Sirius the brightest of all the fixed stars. Along the African coast from Egypt to Morocco, it will *now* be visible at some season low on the horizon at transit. As we steer northwards, it will sink lower, when visible at night, grazing the horizon at transit when we pass beyond a parallel of latitude which approximately bisects Sicily. Further north, it will rise above the horizon

at no time in the year. The star lore of neither the priests of Egypt nor those of Iraq could anticipate this experience. Everywhere in the territories familiar to them, Canopus is now visible at some time in the year.

Nowhere on our cruises, shall we see all the bright stars of the *Southern Cross* (Fig. 43), but we may see the one labelled γ *Crucis*, if we remain south of a line near the Lebanon-Israel frontier and close to Haifa (Jaffa). Here it now grazes the horizon at transit. Further north, it never rises above it. This again is an experience beyond the ken of the astronomer priests of remote antiquity. Nor would they be able to anticipate where some stars are and are not circumpolar. Of such, all the stars which recall the letter *W* in the constellation of *Cassiopeia* will be circumpolar only while we are now cruising north of a line which lies a few miles from Beirut in Syria. In the equally familiar constellation of the Great Bear, all the bright stars other than the one (η in *Ursa major*) at the tip of its tail will be circumpolar north of the island now called Minorca.

We shall need to cruise a little north of Minorca to see the tail star graze the horizon at lower culmination. Both the *clock stars* (α and β) of the Great Bear will still be circumpolar so long as we keep our course north of Beirut. If our course takes us into the Gulf of Genoa or of Venice, we shall be able to greet the bright star *Capella* in the constellation of Auriga nightly throughout the year; but south of a line midway between Ravenna on the Adriatic and Leghorn on the west coast of Italy, it will sink below the horizon at lower culmination. Hence it will be visible only during part of the year.

The stars named in the last few paragraphs are those we should now see in the positions stated on courses traversed by the first seafaring folk who became familiar with the boundaries of the Mediterranean. That the picture was different in their time need not force us to revise our estimate of the stock in trade of new star lore they could transmit by word of mouth to the apprentice pilot before any ships ventured, as we shall now venture under modern skies, beyond the Pillars of Hercules. Again, we must remind ourselves that we should not witness the same event at different parts of the year. What follows is therefore a *composite* picture.

We have a firm foothold in history, if we now follow a northerly course such as that of Pytheas (p. 95) at about 300 B.C. When our ship passes west and north (Fig. 44)

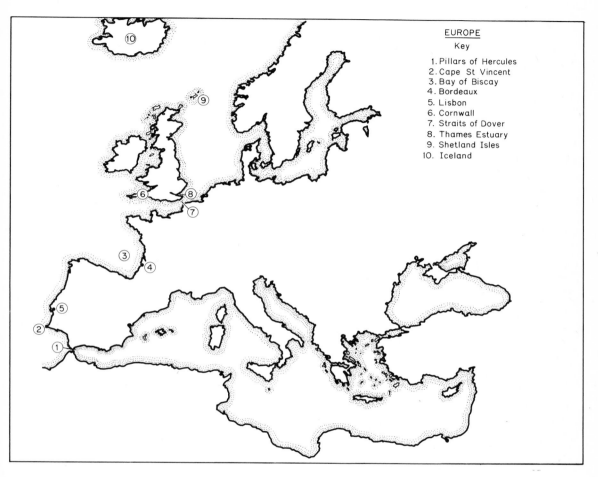

EUROPE
Key

1. Pillars of Hercules
2. Cape St Vincent
3. Bay of Biscay
4. Bordeaux
5. Lisbon
6. Cornwall
7. Straits of Dover
8. Thames Estuary
9. Shetland Isles
10. Iceland

44. Europe

beyond the Pillars of Hercules, no star of the Southern Cross will be visible at any time of the year. As we coast along what is now Portugal, Canopus, still just visible grazing the horizon at transit for a short season at Cape St. Vincent, will have disappeared for all time before we reach Lisbon. We shall not, indeed, encounter any experience new to crews which have coasted off North Italy till we have cruised along the Bay of Biscay beyond Bordeaux. Capella, like all stars in Cassiopeia and in the Great Bear, being now circumpolar, will be perpetually above the horizon of the night sky.

While we continue to cruise within the confines of the Mediterranean, our only likely experience of very conspicuous stars exactly overhead at transit will have been *Castor* and *Pollux* in the constellation of *Gemini* (the Heavenly Twins); but if we have penetrated to the northern limit of the Adriatic above Trieste we shall have already seen *Capella* at upper culmination directly overhead. When north-bound beyond Bordeaux, we shall again see it directly overhead at transit. Between Cape St. Vincent and Lisbon, *Vega* will have reached its highest altitude, being briefly a zenith star at transit. If we aim for the tin mines of Cornwall, other surprises are in store for us as we approach out goal.

Near its southernmost limit, the star *Algol* in the constellation of Perseus will for the first time now graze the horizon at lower culmination. If we venture further eastwards and again north at the Straits of Dover, *Vega* will become a circumpolar star, when we pass the Thames estuary. Coasting along the east of Britain, we shall greet *Castor* as a circumpolar star when we approach the northern boundary of Scotland. On reaching the Shetland Isles we shall be taking our last look at the Southern star *Formalhaut* now visible only for a very short period in winter even in the extreme South of Britain. Midway between the Shetlands and Iceland, *Pollux*, the co-twin of *Castor* will graze the northern horizon at lower culmination. If, like Pytheas, we still press on to the northern limit of *Thule* (the Greek name for Iceland), we shall be in the Arctic belt, where the sun never sets at midsummer and never rises at midwinter.

Still under modern skies, let us now cover the route (Fig. 45) of the Phoenician cargoes commissioned by the Pharaoh Necho. There, a new and different experience of the sun's behaviour awaits us. Actually, this voyage

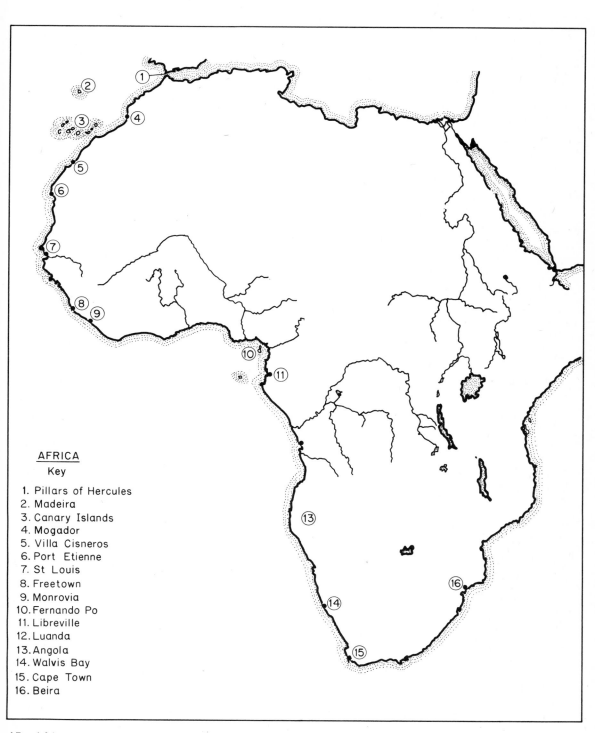

AFRICA
  Key

 1. Pillars of Hercules
 2. Madeira
 3. Canary Islands
 4. Mogador
 5. Villa Cisneros
 6. Port Etienne
 7. St Louis
 8. Freetown
 9. Monrovia
10. Fernando Po
11. Libreville
12. Luanda
13. Angola
14. Walvis Bay
15. Cape Town
16. Beira

45. Africa

seems to have started in the Red Sea and ended in the Mediterranean. It will bring more sharply into focus the relation between the mariner's experience of Mediterranean navigation and of a southerly cruise beyond the Pillars of Hercules, if we here follow the course in reverse order, starting at Alexandria and ending in the Red Sea. The first part of our journey beyond Gibraltar and as far as Sierra Leone will then be the course traversed by Hanno of Carthage. In what follows, as before, we shall condense the experience of several such voyages along our route at very different times of the year.

When we now reach Mogador on the Moroccan coast, *Castor* will be a zenith star, as is its co-twin *Pollux* when we reach the Canary Islands. After we have sailed South less than 70 miles from Mogador, the four bright stars of the Southern Cross will at some time of the year be visible. Little is again worthy of record for our purpose till we anchor near Villa Cisneros in the Rio de Oro (Spanish Sahara). Here we shall see *Alcyone,* the brightest star of the *Pleiades* (Seven Sisters) directly overhead at transit, and within 50 miles further south, *Hamal* in the constellation of the Ram will be a zenith star.

Between the two locations last mentioned, we see, for the first time in our lives, the sun directly overhead on what is there the longest day of the year, i.e. midsummer. We express the occurrence nowadays by saying that we have reached the *Tropic of Cancer*. If we dally in the region which lies south of this latitude and north of Walvis Bay in South West Africa we shall be able to bring home our tallest traveller's tale. On these coasts, there will be one period of the year in which the noon shadow of the sun points north and another in which it points south.

If we coast between Port Etienne and St. Louis along

what was till recently French West Africa, *Arcturus* becomes a zenith star; and if we cast anchor outside St. Louis itself, *Aldebaran* will also be directly overhead at transit. Just beyond Bathurst in Gambia *Regulus*, and off shore near Freetown in Sierra Leone *Altair*, become zenith stars. Within a hundred miles south of Freetown and north of Monrovia in Liberia the bright star *Betelgeuse* in the constellation of Orion has also become a zenith star.

If we keep in the wake of recognisable seabirds following us not far out of sight of land, our course now turns east. There is then little of interest to record till we pass Fernando Po and reach Libreville in what used to be the French Congo, now the Gabonese Republic. Anchored outside this, we shall see the star δ in the belt of Orion transit at the zenith, and at the zenith we shall see the noon sun of the equinoxes. Here also we shall see our Mariner's Pole Star just grazing the northern sky limit. We have then reached the equator; and we have left behind us regions where our own Pole Star is visible at any time.

Shortly before we anchor off Luanda in the Congo, *Rigel* in Orion will transit directly overhead; and, when we are approaching the southern limit of Angola (Portuguese West Africa), Sirius will also have become a zenith star. When we are within 40 miles of Walvis Bay in South West Africa, we are where the noon sun of our own mid-winter (December 21) day is directly overhead. We have now reached the *Tropic of Capricorn*, where June 21 is our shortest day. While we continue to steer south, the sun's shadow at noon will henceforth point always south.

Almost exactly at the northern coastal boundary of the South African Republic the clock-hand star α in the Great Bear ceases to be visible at any time. Within 100 miles of its northern boundary, *Formalhaut* shines directly overhead as it crosses our celestial meridian. As we approach Cape Town, and before we round the Cape, the clock star β of the Great Bear will have sunk below the horizon at all times, as will all the stars of Cassiopeia.

On the voyage up the coast to the northerly limit of the Red Sea, we shall witness the same changes of the heavens in reverse. After being so long in a region where the sun's noon shadow always points South, and where December 21 is the longest day, we come again to a belt where the shadow of the noon sun points North for part of the year bounded by two days when the noon sun is directly overhead. Before we reach Beira in Portuguese East Africa on our northward-bound course, we are once more in a region where the sun's shadow at noon points always to the North. Once again, December 21 is the shortest day of the year, and June 21 the longest.

To be sure, the Ancient Mariner of three thousand years ago would not see the same night sky, though he would see the same story of the sun's vagaries, as we have done on our twentieth-century cruise. None the less, he would have reached, as was correctly interpreted current knowledge by the time, and probably earlier than that of Aristotle, two inescapable conclusions, neither of which is intelligible on the assumption that the earth is a flat disc. Such an interpretation was good enough for the priestly purpose of forecasting solar eclipses to a credulous and illiterate public. It could not satisfy the now literate master mariner.

If we did indeed live on a flat circular disc, we should admittedly see some stars nearer the horizon at transit as we approached the edge of the disc. What we should not see is that totally different stars would become more and more visible and higher above the horizon as others disappeared. Besides that, our sun would always cast its noon shadow to where we see the circumpolar stars seemingly revolving in the direction we call north. We should never reach a region where it pointed south nor pass through a region where it pointed one way at one part of the year and the other way at another.

To be sure, neither fact conclusively proves that the earth is a perfect sphere, or nearly so. What each shows is that the surface of the earth is everywhere a curved surface. If so, the simplest, and for reasons we shall later see, the most credible attitude we can take to the world we live in is that our earth is indeed a spherical body. As often happens in the history of science, the simplest explanation, with trivial emendations, turns out to be the best, and it is an economy of time and effort to start by assuming this is so. Conclusive proof requires measurement of the distance corresponding to a degree of longitude at the equator and a degree of latitude everywhere else to be approximately equal. Many centuries had to elapse before it was established that this is very nearly true.

It is no accident that belief in the sphericity of the earth took shape among the maritime rather than the mainland Greeks and at a time when war did not as yet sap resources of trade on sea routes. When Pythagoras taught that the earth was a perfect sphere, he was indeed nearer to the truth than are current school books which speak of the earth as a so-called spheroid flattened at both ends like an orange. The fact that its polar and equatorial radii are slightly different impressed itself on Newton's successors because he had predicted it as a consequence of the earth's rotation on its polar axis. The fact is that the difference ($13\frac{1}{3}$ miles) is less than a healthy day's walk in fine weather. An observer on the moon would need good optical equipment to detect it.

What we have learned about the antiquity of Stonehenge in Chapter 3 has taught us that a thousand years separates the date when there was first maritime trade beyond the boundaries of the Mediterranean through the Pillars of Hercules from the great leap forward about 500 B.C. when a literate class of master mariners and traders first appears on the stage of history. During this interval, there must have been very many voyages of the sort described in this chapter. Captain pilots of ships would have traversed the same courses at very different times of the year. Just as the astronomer priests inherited a treasury of sky lore through oral tradition from camp fire vigils of many millennia before the written record of the temple takes shape, the now literate Founding Fathers of the Greek contribution inherited through oral tradition a vast repository of geographical lore from many centuries of scanning the night sky in different latitudes by seafarers who themselves were largely letterless.

6 **Maritime Geography and Maritime Astronomy**

The recognition that the earth is a spherical body poised in space carried with it certain consequences in the light of what the ancient mariner, when set on a course north and south of the homeland, had learned about changes of climate, length of day and length of the sun's noon shadow on particular days of the year in different regions. To Parmenides, born at Elea in the Greek-speaking south of Italy, tradition attributes the suggestion of dividing the world into five parallel zones roughly corresponding to what we now call the arctic, north temperate, tropical, south temperate and antarctic belts. Parmenides flourished about 450 B.C. Like Herodotus, himself a great traveller, he was the first Greek historian on record to divide the land mass into the continents Europe, Asia and Africa.

A century later, Aristotle defines the north temperate zone as extending from the Tropic of Cancer to the Arctic circle. Here at least dimly, the notion of latitude is beginning to intrude in the stock in trade of information available to a literate public. We have already seen how it emerged in the everyday experiences of pilots who first coasted along the west coasts of Africa and Europe. In modern terms, we may express this by saying that the rising and setting positions of the stars, their zenith distances at transit and the sun's noon altitude on a particular day of the year vary consistently with latitude and with latitude alone.

Today a ship's captain and officers have access to tables from which they can calculate by recourse to a very simple formula their latitude if they have determined the local zenith distance of any star at transit or, on a particular date, that of the noon sun. Given their latitude and longitude they can therefore locate their position on a map. In its modern sense, the word latitude came into use about two hundred years later, but master mariners during the lifetime of Aristotle were navigating by latitude in all but name.

Before ships turned westwards far from land, long voyages, like those of Chapter 5, kept close enough to the coast for sailors to recognise sea-birds which rested there. It therefore sufficed to be able to locate a port by one or other of the astronomical observations in terms of which one defines latitude. For instance, they would know that they were near the equator as their Pole Star nearly sank below the horizon or that they were at the Tropic of Cancer when they reached a port where the noon sun was directly overhead on midsummer day. Though its definition belongs to the period when that of latitude as now defined took shape, the notion of longitude had little relevance to navigation until the time of Columbus.

If the length of the noon shadow and the length of a pillar were equal on March 21 or September 23 of our own calendar, their latitude would be 45° as we now express the fact. Before there were maps in latitude and longitude, i.e. before 150 B.C., it would serve the same purpose to record that the noon sun's zenith distance was 45°, since the sun's zenith distance at noon on the equinoxes is equal to the observer's latitude.

In effect therefore, the European pilots who first voyaged beyond the Mediterranean navigated by latitude though they did not, as yet, tabulate their records with the same labels as ourselves. Concerning what instruments they used, or when they first recorded the altitude at transit of particular bright stars at particular ports of call, we know nothing with certainty. We do know, however, what they could record when in port—for instance, the sun's noon altitude on one of the solstices or one of the equinoxes in terms of the ratio of the height of a pillar to the length of its shadow.

When we come near the peak of the Greek contribution, as we speak of it in this book, a name mentioned much by its successors is illustrious as one of its new personnel of literate mariners. Unhappily, the works of Pytheas, like those of Democritus, are lost, and we know of his discoveries only by citations and references to them by later writers. He was a native of Marseilles, then a Greek colony and according to Professor Farrington recorded its latitude within a small fraction of a degree. More correctly, one may say that he recorded the noon sun's altitude on the summer solstice. In this sense, later writers credit him with fixing the latitude of several ports which he visited in his celebrated voyage to Iceland.

According to his successors, Pytheas was a contemporary of Alexander the Great. If so, his lifetime must have overlapped that of Aristotle, though there is no indication that they ever met. The lifetime of both would have witnessed the commemorative building of Alexandria, soon to become a great centre of maritime trade on the fringe of a vastly older civilisation. There Greek was the medium of scientific communication. None the less, Alexandrian culture developed in a new environment to meet a new challenge and with new resources of personnel.

With Pytheas, what we here call the Greek contribution (p. 64) thus comes to its climax. According to his commentators, he was the first writer to recognise the relation of the tides to the phases of the moon and to draw attention to their periodic fluctuations, i.e. spring and neap tides. He seems also to have been the first writer to record the differences between the length of the longest day in different parts of Britain. From the same sources, we learn that he recorded the way in which climate changes as one journeys northwards from the coast of Spain to the Arctic Circle.

At the end of the Greek period, i.e. 300 B.C., astronomical knowledge other than local variations of the altitude of the heavenly bodies at transit was of practical importance in terms of the world's work only in so far as it led to a reform of the calendar. To understand it, we must retrace our steps to the beginnings of city life in Egypt and Iraq. Till a comparatively late date, it had been the custom in Iraq to intercalate from time to time extra 30-day months to keep a 360-day year in step with the seasons. This, of course, is on all fours with our addition of an extra day (February 29) every four years to what is otherwise the 365 day year of the Egyptian calendar. Before 432 B.C. the system of adjustment used in Athens was to intercalate 3 extra 30-day months in an 8 year cycle of solar years reckoned from solstice to corresponding solstice or equinox to corresponding equinox and, as we now say, averaging nearly exactly $365\frac{1}{4}$ days.

The reform of 432 B.C. attributed to the Athenian astronomer Meton, and known accordingly as the Metonic cycle, was the insertion of seven lunar months, reckoned from one full or new* moon to the next, in a sequence of 19 solar years. In terms of what we now know to be the mean interval between two full moons,

---

*The temple astronomers of Iraq reckoned the month as the interval between successive occasions when the moon was first visible as a thin crescentric streak after the end of the last quarter, i.e. so-called new moon. This is a more accurate method of recording the interval than to base it on the full moon. There is more margin for error in deciding exactly when the moon is full.

i.e. 29 days, 12 hours, and nearly 46 minutes, this device makes the average length of the lunar month correct within 2 minutes. However, we cannot assume that astronomers at that date recognised that a solar year is almost exactly 365 days and 6 hours. Later writers attribute this to Eudoxus who was born about 25 years later.

Though the division of the diurnal cycle into 24 units was a legacy of Egyptian astronomy, the Egyptian hour, originally based on the sun's shadow, varied in length throughout daylight and at corresponding times at different parts of the year. Before the introduction of the Moslem sun dial, still seen in Europe on church towers, there was indeed no way of calibrating the direction of the sun's shadow so that it registered hours of equal length. To record an hour as one twenty-fourth of the interval between two noons, the Greeks used *clepsydras* (water clocks). These were vessels which emptied when filled to the brim in an hour or fixed fraction of an hour. In Iraq, this device had long been in use and a vessel probably used for the same purpose has been unearthed at Karnak in Egypt. Its date was about 1500 B.C. It seems that the Chinese also had water clocks at about that time.

Though astronomers were later to put more and more elaborate water clocks to their own uses, the Greeks used them first with a different end in view. Instead of the chairman's bell to put pay to a filibuster, the clepsydra regulated how long the political orator, the counsel for prosecution or defence and the exponent of philosophical speculation could continue to punish the audience.

According to Professor Neugebauer, our leading living expert on the mathematical lore of the temple cloisters in Iraq, the 19-year cycle for regulating the calendar was in use there at about the date of the Athens reform. So it may not have been an indigenous Greek device. At about the same time, or maybe earlier, the astronomer priests of Iraq were responsible for another innovation. The astrological columns of the tabloids have made us all familiar with it, though few of us really know what the astrologer means when he (or she) says that the sun is in Leo or Cancer.

In the earliest civilisations from China to Egypt, the custodians of the calendar recognised particular star clusters whose rising and setting positions correspond to those of the sun at different times of the year. Those of Iraq at some time before 400 B.C. designated twelve equally spaced constellations, those we call the *zodiacal*, to keep track of the sun's rising and setting position in every one of the twelve thirty-day months of the lunar year (Fig. 30). Their names are *Cancer* (the Crab), *Leo* (the Lion), *Virgo* (the Virgin), *Libra* (the Scales), *Scorpio* (the Scorpion), *Sagittarius*, (the Archer), *Capricornus* (the Goat), *Aquarius* (the Water Carrier), *Pisces* (the Fish), *Aries* (the Ram), *Taurus* (the Bull), *Gemini* (the Twins).

With the exception of *Gemini* with its two bright stars Castor and Pollux, none of these star clusters present to the eye so conspicuously a pattern as the Great Bear, Orion or the Pleiades; and their delimitation to cover approximately 30° of the sun's track is quite arbitrary. At the time when the zodiac first comes into the picture, the sun was in Cancer on midsummer day, in Capricorn on midwinter day, in Aries on the vernal equinox and in Libra on the autumnal equinox. To make clear what *in* signifies in this context, it will suffice to consider what one means by saying that the sun is in Cancer. It implies both that the sun's rising and setting positions will correspond to those of some star in the constellation of

Cancer six months later and that noon corresponds to the time of transit of some star in the constellation of Cancer. The latter event will, of course, be invisible since it happens in daylight.

The signs (i.e. constellations) of the zodiac have left one lasting impression on our vocabulary. At the time when the zodiac came into use, the noon sun in Cancer was directly overhead on midsummer day at what we call accordingly the Tropic of Cancer. At what we call the Tropic of Capricorn, the noon sun in Capricorn was directly overhead on what is midwinter day in the northern hemisphere.

The zodiacal constellations define a wide belt within which the moon, sun and five planets of antiquity (*Mercury, Venus, Mars, Jupiter,* and *Saturn*) appear to move at different speeds. Thus the sun completes its cycle in a year, the moon in a month. Astronomy took a great leap forward when measurement of the sun's altitude at different seasons located within this belt an imaginary circle, the *ecliptic,* which delineates the sun's apparent annual retreat below the eastern horizon.

Before we can do justice to how astronomers such as Eudoxus and his contemporaries in Iraq sought to make an abstract model of all the motions of the heavenly bodies, we must pause to make clear why we here, as already elsewhere, speak of the sun's *apparent* track above and below the local horizon. The reader may well be confused because so many popular expositions of astronomy start with, or assume, the *heliocentric* in contradistinction to the *geocentric* interpretation of what we see when scanning the skies. The first means how an imaginary observer on the sun would interpret the motions of the earth, stars and planets most effortlessly. The second means how an earth-bound observer like ourselves interprets with least effort the behaviour of sun, moon, and fixed stars, though not of the planets.

In what sense the first view, which has widely gained acceptance only during the past four hundred years or so, is more true than the second need not concern us here. The latter sufficed for the design of the Gregorian Calendar still in use today and for the lay-out of the Mercator projection map first issued in the half century after the Columbian voyages. For most practical purposes relevant to the making of clocks, calendars, the charts of the mariner or maps of the United Nations publications, the second and older view is more convenient.

It is not more convenient if our aim is to plot the path of the planets, which change their positions among the fixed stars, seeming at some times to move in one, and at other times in the opposite, direction. This was an issue of no concern to navigators before they sailed westwards into the uncharted Atlantic; but it did become of considerable practical importance to Columbus and his successors who relied considerably on planetary observations to determine longitude. Since the invention of the chronometer, such observations have ceased to be of interest with that end in view. It is now simpler for seamen or air pilots to adopt the *geocentric* view, when making their calculations, as if we ourselves are at rest while the sun, the moon and the stars revolve above us from one margin of the horizon to its opposite.

Fortunately for our own generation, everyday experience makes it much easier than it was for the contemporaries of Columbus and Copernicus to realise why calculations based on two different ways of looking at the same problem can be consistent. When one of two trains in a station begins to move on a parallel track, a passenger in either may rightly or wrongly conclude that he or she is in motion. If one can see through the window of one's own an object on the station, one can confidently decide which is at rest and which is not. Otherwise, the two possibilities are equally plausible, and the distinction is irrelevant to correct calculation of their distance apart. We have no such station to guide our judgement when we gaze into the immensity of the heavens above us.

According to the geocentric view, the sun participates with the fixed stars in a diurnal motion around an axis which passes through the Celestial Pole (p. 8) and it executes more slowly an annual motion in the reverse direction along the Ecliptic. According to the alternative, now accepted, view, the diurnal appearances are due to the rotation of the earth on an axis which joins the terrestrial poles to the Celestial Pole and the annual cycle is due to the earth's movement around the sun in an orbit in the same plane as the Ecliptic. Before the seventeenth century of our own era, there was no direct evidence for the rotation of the earth and before the nineteenth century there was no direct evidence for the earth's revolution in an orbit round the sun. Astronomers first rejected the geocentric view solely because no amount of mathematical ingenuity could provide a means of forecasting the position of the planets with great precision. The alternative interpretation is both vastly more simple and vastly more precise.

We may now properly round off our narrative of the Greek contribution with a reference to Eudoxus, who was born on an island off the coast of Asia Minor, studied under Plato for a short period and left the Academy to travel in Egypt and elsewhere. He was probably influenced by conclusions already reached in the temples of Iraq. Like those of Democritus, his works have not survived the ravages of wars. To reconstruct his picture of the universe we have to rely on the testimony of later astronomers.

The place of Eudoxus in the history of science is noteworthy for two reasons. One is because his own is an early example, indeed the first on record of a device—the physical model—which has played an important role in science. It is also of interest for what it fails to do. All too pure mathematicians have greatly praised Eudoxus as a devout pupil of Plato for all he did to demote geometry as a science of measurement to the status of argumentative logic. This model universe of Eudoxus is in line with his preoccupation as a pupil of Plato. What remains discloses no trace of measurement. Its author's main concern was with the direction in which the heavenly bodies seem to move, but at what angles and what distances is not in the picture.

Eudoxus conceived his model universe as an assemblage of 26 translucent and spherical shells moving at different speeds not all in the same direction. To each of the five planets then known, he assigned an envelope of four shells, to the moon three, the sun two, and the fixed stars one.

It is more easy to assess the level which Greek astronomy had reached before 300 B.C., if we forget about the shells of the model except in so far as the number of them gives us a clue to what was then known about the apparent motions of the heavenly bodies, as seen from the viewpoint of an earth-centred observer. Since all subsequent attempts to elaborate the model universe of Eudoxus to give a wholly satisfactory account of planetary motions proved inadequate, we need not here concern ourselves with the planets.

With that behind us, let us first ask what Greek

astronomers at 300 B.C. postulated about how the sun and moon participate with the fixed stars in a diurnal circular motion. From the viewpoint of an observer at the centre of the earth, they rotate about an axis passing through the Celestial and Terrestrial Poles at right angles to the common plane of the Terrestrial and Celestial Equator. The direction of this rotation is from east to west above the horizon. Both sun and moon have also a motion in the opposite direction, and in a path inclined to the Celestial Equator. The period of this motion of the sun relative to the fixed stars was recognised correctly by Eudoxus as approximately 365 days 6 hours. In contra-distinction to its period of, roughly, $29\frac{1}{2}$ days, relative to the sun (so-called synodic month), i.e. interval between two new or two full moons, the moon's period (so-called *sidereal* month) relative to the fixed stars is very nearly $27\frac{1}{3}$ days. We may charitably assume that these estimates were stock in trade of Greek astronomy.

To account for the interval between eclipses at the time of Eudoxus, Greek astronomers seem to have made two assumptions. One is that the respective paths of the annual and monthly retreat of the sun and moon are not equally inclined to the Celestial Equator. *Vis-à-vis* the scorn of Plato for astronomers (p. 73) who made measure-ments, it is mentionable that we have no evidence that Greek astronomers of this period had made actual measurements of either angle. A second assumption which accounts for Eudoxus equipping the moon with a third revolving shell will be easier to understand after a brief digression on how eclipses can happen.

Both a lunar eclipse, when we see the earth's shadow between the moon and sun, or a solar eclipse, when we see the moon like a disc between ourselves and the sun (Figs. 46, 47, and 48) can happen only when the earth,

46. Eclipses.
    A. total solar eclipse,
    B. earth's shadow seen
    as moon is at beginning
    of lunar eclipse
    C. total lunar eclipse.

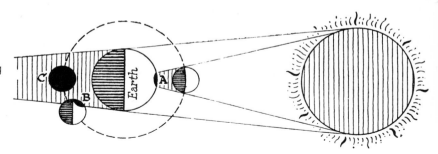

moon, and sun are in one and the same straight line and therefore in the same plane, i.e. that of the Ecliptic. This cannot happen simultaneously at all places. On account of the earth's rotation, as we now say, and of the apparent movements of the moon and sun between the times when the three bodies are actually on the same straight line, an eclipse is a local phenomenon in the sense that it may be partial or unseen in one place and total in another.

Even so, if the moon's orbit were exactly in the plane of the ecliptic, there would be at some locality a total eclipse of the sun at new moon, when the moon would be in line between earth and sun. There would also at some locality be a total lunar eclipse at full moon when the earth is between the sun and the moon. This is not so. Hence, the inclination of the moon's track to the Ecliptic is beyond dispute. As we now know, the inclination is about 5° (Fig. 49).

Without precise measurements of either the *Obliquity of the Ecliptic*, i.e. the inclination of the Ecliptic to the Celestial Equator, or the inclination of the moon's orbit to the Ecliptic itself, we can thus conclude that the two

47. Moon eclipse, seen in
    East Germany.
    A picture of the moon
    in eclipse as seen at
    the Solwerin Obser-
    vatory in East
    Germany. These
    pictures were taken at
    2.18 am, 2.29 am. and
    2.41 am

48. Solar eclipse

49

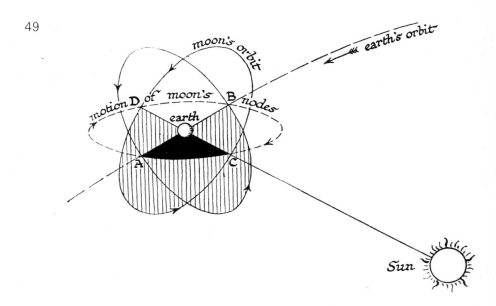

planes must intersect at two points called the lunar *nodes*. In contradistinction to explaining why eclipses are not monthly events, we have to make another assumption to account for when eclipses *do* occur, namely that the nodes themselves rotate. This is presumably the *raison d'être* for equipping the model of Eudoxus' moon with a third shell. If the nodes were static, i.e. the moon's position relative to the fixed stars remained the same when it crossed the Ecliptic, it would be a comparatively simple matter to forecast the interval between two occasions when the sun and earth were both in line with a node and hence with the moon. In that event eclipses of either sort would be more frequent than is actually so.

A solar eclipse can occur only when the new moon is at a node (Fig. 49) and a lunar eclipse only when a full moon is at one. Another will occur when the number of subsequent revolutions of the node relative to the sun is exactly the same as the number of subsequent lunar (synodic) months. The period of the revolution of the nodes relative to the sun is approximately 346.2 days; that of the lunar month approximately 29.53 days. Thus, 19 revolutions of the nodes and 223 lunar months are both equivalent to roughly 6585 days, a little over 18 years.

Tradition attributes the knowledge of this cycle of 18-plus years to the priestly astronomers of Iraq at a date earlier than 1500 B.C. From what we know of their well-paid success in forecasting such auspicious occurrences, this is credible less for any theories they might have spun than for practical reasons based on temple records kept for centuries. To have even a tolerably precise theory, one would require measurements of two sorts. We have no sufficient direct evidence that Greek astronomers had themselves made or had taken over either of them from an earlier civilisation.

Two centuries later, when the Alexandrian successors of Eudoxus began to reinstate measurements of distances and angles in a modified form of the model, a third shell was requisite either for the sun or for the sphere of the fixed stars. Just as we may speak of two points where the moon's orbit intersects with the plane of the Ecliptic as lunar nodes, we may speak of two points where the Ecliptic cuts the plane of the Celestial Equator as solar nodes. The Alexandrian successors of Eudoxus discovered, or learned, as we shall in the next instalment of *The Beginnings of Science*, from their Greek speaking colleagues in Iraq, that these solar nodes also revolve in the same direction as the apparent motion of the fixed stars, but far more slowly than the lunar nodes, indeed at less than a thousandth of the rate at which the nodes of the moon itself shift.

Accordingly, it could be detected in a human lifetime

only with instruments vastly more sensitive than were available before the Christian era. It was demonstrable, when first recognised only from the testimony of temple library records kept up to date for several centuries. Such is the 25,000 year cycle called the *Precession of the Equinoxes* mentioned in this book on more than one occasion previously. One result of precession is that different stars may be more or less near the celestial pole and different constellations may be circumpolar at different epochs. In 3000 B.C., the star α Draconis was a good pole star, as was Vega about 1300 B.C. Our own pole star is the star at the end of the tail in the constellation of *Ursa Minor* (Little Bear).

After the death of Eudoxus and of Aristotle, science went into decline on the mainland of Greece and in the maritime Greek-speaking colonies where atomic speculation was still-born. By shortly after 300 B.C. astronomy, together with scientific geography and optics, made a fresh start in the cosmopolitan port of Alexandria. The consequences of this contributed greatly to the voyages of Columbus. The period between Alexander the Great and Columbus is the topic of the next volume of *The Beginnings of Science*.

50. Romantic nineteenth
     century engraving of
     how Greeks imagined
     the Pillars of Hercules

Glossary of Technical Terms

For convenience of definition, the order of the following is not alphabetical.

CELESTIAL SPHERE

If our sole concern is the direction in which we have to look to locate one, relative distances of different stars from the observer are irrelevant and it is convenient from a geometrical point of view to imagine them located on the surface of a vast sphere concentric with the earth itself and revolving round it in 24 hours.

CELESTIAL EQUATOR

An imaginary circle on the Celestial Sphere bounding the plane of the earth's equator.

CELESTIAL MERIDIAN

An imaginary semicircle joining the north and south limits of the horizon with its highest point directly above the observer.

CELESTIAL POLES

The two points where the earth's polar axis would cut the celestial sphere if extended indefinitely in both directions.

ECLIPTIC

An imaginary circle on the celestial sphere intersecting with the Celestial Equator at an angle of approximately $23\frac{1}{2}°$. The 2 points of intersection locate the sun's position at the Equinoxes (see below). This circle defines the changing positions of the sun in its annual retreat through the seasons.

EQUINOXES

The two days (March 21 and Sept 23) when the sun is directly overhead at the terrestrial equator, and so called because the hours of light and darkness are then approximately equal. On these two days the sun rises and sets almost exactly East and West.

SOLSTICES

The two days (June 21 and Dec 21) when the sun is furthest from the Celestial Equator and is directly overhead respectively at the tropics of Cancer and Capricorn.

ZODIAC

Twelve star clusters which the ecliptic intersects.

ZENITH

The point where the observer's plumb line would meet the Celestial Meridian, if extended indefinitely.

TRANSIT

A celestial body is said to transit (or be at transit) when it lies on the Celestial Meridian and is then at its maximum altitude above the horizon plane.

ZENITH STAR

A star which transits at the zenith of the observer's locality and can therefore be seen throughout any clear night throughout the year.

PRECESSION OF THE EQUINOXES

From the standpoint of an imaginary solar observer, the earth's axis wobbles like that of a spinning top when coming to rest. From an earth-centred viewpoint the points of intersection of the Ecliptic with the Celestial Equator shift very slowly, completing a cycle in about 26,000 years. On this account, the rising and setting positions of the so-called fixed stars change—albeit very slowly—in the course of time.